THE COMMONWEALTH AND INTERNATIONAL LIBRARY

Joint Chairmen of the Honorary Editorial Advisory Board

SIR ROBERT ROBINSON, O.M., F.R.S., LONDON

DEAN ATHELSTAN SPILHAUS, MINNESOTA

Publisher: ROBERT MAXWELL, M.C., M.P.

ELECTRICAL ENGINEERING DIVISION

General Editor: N. HILLER

RADIO AND LINE TRANSMISSION

VOLUME 1

RADIO AND
LINE TRANSMISSION

VOLUME 1

by

D. RODDY, M.Sc., C.Eng., M.I.E.E., A.M.I.E.R.E.

PERGAMON PRESS

OXFORD · LONDON · EDINBURGH · NEW YORK

TORONTO · SYDNEY · PARIS · BRAUNSCHWEIG

Pergamon Press Ltd., Headington Hill Hall, Oxford
4 & 5 Fitzroy Square, London W.1
Pergamon Press (Scotland) Ltd., 2 & 3 Teviot Place, Edinburgh 1
Pergamon Press Inc., 44 – 01 21st Street, Long Island City, New York 11101
Pergamon of Canada, Ltd., 6 Adelaide Street East, Toronto, Ontario
Pergamon Press (Aust.) Pty. Ltd., 20 – 22 Margaret Street,
Sydney, New South Wales
Pergamon Press S.A.R.L., 24 rue des Écoles, Paris 5e
Vieweg & Sohn GmbH, Burgplatz 1, Braunschweig

CONTENTS

Chapter 9. Rectifier and Demodulator (Detector) Circuits   147

Chapter 10. Amplifiers   160

Chapter 11. Tuned Circuit Oscillators   192

FOREWORD

THIS volume is one of a series of texts written for technicians in the electrical engineering industry. In particular, the three volumes on *Radio and Line Transmission* will cover the new recommended syllabuses of the CGLI Course No. 49 for telecommunication technicians. They will also be suitable for electrical technicians specializing in radio communications and as an introductory course for the senior technician on national certificate courses.

In order to cater for this wide range of courses it has been necessary to extend some chapters and to deal with some topics in more detail than is indicated in the CGLI published syllabuses. Nevertheless, it is hoped that the reader will find these extensions interesting and that it will help to prepare him for the more advanced work.

N. HILLER

Cambridge   *Editor*

AUTHOR'S PREFACE

THIS book is based on lectures given to telecommunication technicians, both in the U.K. and overseas. It has been the author's experience that while student technicians may be unhappy with the more mathematical treatments of their subject, they do look for a fairly rigorous verbal treatment, and it is hoped that the book goes some way towards providing this. When new to a subject, the student is bound to encounter new words, and here the use of a good dictionary cannot be over-emphasized. An understanding of the origins of a word often gives rise to new avenues of thought around a subject.

Grateful acknowledgements are made to: H.M. Postmaster-General for permission to reproduce Fig 12.5, for the use of the P.O. Engineering Dept. Educational Pamphlets, and for providing actual components for inspection; Mullard Limited who kindly provided the diagrams for Figs 8.9, 8.28, 8.30, as well as much descriptive detail; Erie Resistor Limited who prepared the blocks for Figs. 5.2, 5.3(a), 5.5, 5.9(a), and for providing a great deal of other useful information; City & Guild's of London Institute for permission to use past examination questions, although the solutions which are given are the sole responsibility of the author; the many other manufacturers and Institutions who supplied information which although not used directly nevertheless has been of value.

The author is also glad to acknowledge the free use that has been made of the numerous more advanced textbooks and other technical publications for which individual acknowledgement would be very difficult.

Stafford, 1967   D. R.

CHAPTER 1

WAVES

1.1. Introduction

Communications by means of sound is an essential feature in the progress of man and in the growth of civilizations. Today this is apparent in the natural and highly developed art of speech, and in more contrived forms involving codes such as Morse.

Wave motion is an important concept in the study of communications methods. The pressure variations produced by sound execute a wave motion, and these in turn may be used to generate or control an electromagnetic wave. Fortunately, many of the characteristics of wave motion apply in general to all types of waves.

1.2. Wave motion

Probably the most familiar example of wave motion is that of surface waves on water. With these, a succession of "humps" appear to move across the surface of the water. Closer examination of the water surface shows that in any one region the water rises and falls without actually moving away from the region. The rise and fall disturbance passes smoothly from one region to the next, giving the appearance of a movement of water across the surface.

If the disturbance is measured, its size (or magnitude) will be found to depend on (a) the instant at which it is measured, and (b) the particular region at which it is measured. If, for example, surface waves are set up on water and one particular region is viewed through a narrow slit (as in Fig. 1.1), the height of the water as seen through the slit will indicate the rise and fall variation with time, although the apparent motion across the surface will not be observed. The height may be measured at given in-

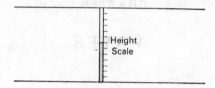

FIG. 1.1. Surface wave variation with time.

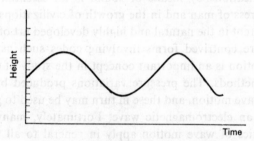

FIG. 1.2. Graphical representation of Fig. 1.1.

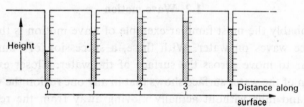

FIG. 1.3. Surface wave variation with distance.

stants of time, and a graph of height against distance plotted as in Fig. 1.2.

If now a number of observers, each viewing a different region from one another, record the height for their region at an agreed instant of time, the picture may be represented as in Fig. 1.3.

Again, a graph may be plotted, but in this instance a graph of height against distance, as shown in Fig. 1.4.

It will be seen that two independent variables must be considered in wave motion, time and distance. Surface waves are perhaps the easiest to visualize since, in fact, they can be seen. Other types of waves are within common experience, sound waves

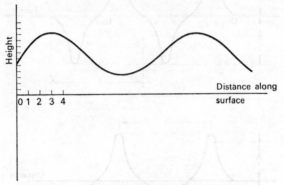

FIG. 1.4. Graphical representation of Fig. 1.3.

and heat waves being examples. Time-and-distance graphs may be drawn for these as for any type of wave function. In describing wave motion it is obviously an advantage to use terms which are easily measured or determined from measurements, and which can be applied to any type of wave in general. The important terms describing wave motion are defined in § 1.3 below.

1.3. Important definitions

The **amplitude** of the wave is the maximum or *peak value* the wave reaches, and is shown as A in Fig. 1.5.

When the wave disturbance is plotted against time, as in Fig. 1.2, it is generally found that a pattern repeats itself in the graph. The time required for *one complete cycle* of the wave is known as the **periodic time**. In Fig. 1.5(a) this is shown as T. The periodic time may in fact be measured between any two points on the curve covering a complete cycle, and not just the points shown in Fig. 1.5(a).

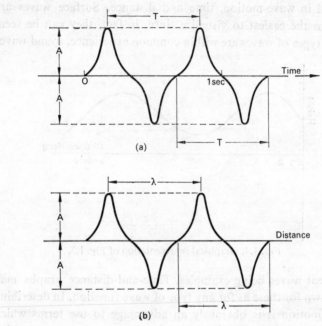

FIG. 1.5. The quantities defined in wave equations.

The **frequency** of the wave is the *number of cycles which occur in one second*, and is usually denoted by the letter f in telecommunications work. The wave shown in Fig. 1.5(a) has a frequency of $1\frac{1}{2}$ cycles per second (c/s).

Relationship between frequency and periodic time

For a wave of f c/s, one cycle requires a time of $1/f$ sec. But this is also the periodic time, hence

$$T = 1/f. \qquad (1.1)$$

Figure 1.4 shows that the wave disturbance also varies in a regular manner with distance, and hence, corresponding to periodic time, is a quantity known as the **wavelength**. This is the *distance covered by one complete cycle of the wave* and it is given the symbol λ. The wavelength is shown in Fig. 1.5(b).

When a wave disturbance is set up, the wave appears to move outwards and away from the source at a given velocity. If, for convenience, a given peak of the wave is observed, its velocity gives the **velocity of propagation** of the wave.

1.4. Relationship between wavelength, frequency, and velocity of propagation

Let the wavelength be λ metres and the frequency f c/s. Hence

Distance covered by one cycle = λ m.

Therefore distance covered by f cycles = λf m.

But since f cycles occur in 1 sec, then the distance covered in 1 sec by the wave is also λf m.

Therefore velocity = λf m/s

or $$v = \lambda f. \tag{1.2}$$

Equation (1.2) is of fundamental importance in telecommunications and electrical engineering, and its use will be illustrated in later sections.

1.5. Equations for a sine wave

A sine wave is a wave disturbance which, when the time-and-distance curves are plotted, have the same shape as the mathematical curve of *sine* against *angle*. This curve is shown in Fig. 1.6(a) and, directly under this, Fig. 1.6(b) is the sine wave time curve and Fig. 1.6(c) the sine wave distance curve. For simplicity, the sine wave is assumed to be a voltage wave, the instantaneous value of which is represented by e, and the amplitude (or peak value) by E_{max}.

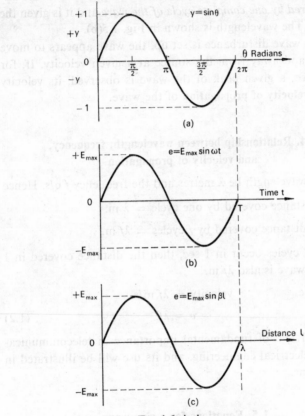

FIG. 1.6. A sine wave.

In Fig. 1.6(b), ω is some constant which connects time t with angle θ. By direct comparison of the curves, it is seen that at the completion of one cycle, $t = T$.

Therefore $\omega T = 2\pi.$

Therefore $\omega = 2\pi/T.$

Hence the voltage variation with time, which is

$$e = E_{max} \sin \omega t,$$

can be written as

$$e = E_{max} \sin \left(\frac{2\pi t}{T}\right). \tag{1.3a}$$

Alternatively, as shown by eqn. (1.1),

$$T = 1/f.$$

Therefore the sinusoidal variation with time can be written as

$$e = E_{max} \sin (2\pi f t). \tag{1.3b}$$

The wave variation with distance can be found in a similar manner. In Fig. 1.6(c) β is some constant which relates distance l to angle θ. Comparing the curves of Fig. 1.6(a) and 1.6(c) at the end of one cycle, it is seen that $l = \lambda$.

Therefore $\qquad\qquad \beta\lambda = 2\pi.$

Therefore $\qquad\qquad \beta = 2\pi/\lambda.$

Substituting this in the distance equation for voltage, which is

$$e = E_{max} \sin \beta l,$$

gives

$$e = E_{max} \sin \left(\frac{2\pi l}{\lambda}\right). \tag{1.4}$$

Thus, eqns. (1.3b) and (1.4) together represent a sine wave of voltage. Very often, in dealing with voltages and currents in circuits, the circuit dimensions (lengths of wires, etc.) are very small compared with a wavelength, and then only the time curve is important. However, it is well to bear in mind that both time and distance are involved with voltage and current waves, as at short wavelengths the distance equation becomes important.

It may be noted that the constant ω is known as the *angular velocity* of the wave, and the constant β as the *phase-shift coefficient*.

In the sine waves of Fig. 1.6, the waveforms are shown as zero at zero time. It will be realized, of course, that some actual time must be chosen to represent zero time, and this need not correspond with the wave being zero. For example, if the time zero is chosen as shown in Fig. 1.7(b), the wave will have some value E_1.

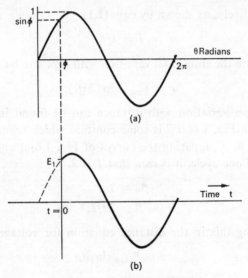

FIG. 1.7. The effect of shifting the zero time origin.

Comparing this value with sine curve shown in Fig. 1.7(a) it will be seen that E_1 corresponds with $y = \sin \phi$. Thus, the general equation for a sinusoidal variation with time can be written as

$$e = E_{\max} \sin (2\pi f t + \phi). \qquad (1.5)$$

A similar argument can be applied to the distance curve.

1.6. Sound waves

Sound is an everyday experience. It is generated by mechanical vibration which causes acceleration of the surrounding air particles. A familiar and convenient example is the loud-speaker in a radio receiver, the sound output of which results from the vibration of the cone. Figure 1.8 shows a sketch of a loud-speaker system.

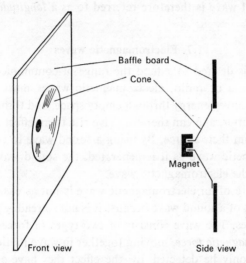

FIG. 1.8. A loud-speaker system.

The velocity of sound waves in air depends on the temperature of the air, the wind velocity (if any), and the humidity. The value measured in still dry air, at 0 °C, is

$$v = 332 \text{ m/s}.$$

It is clear that any substance capable of transmitting pressure changes can transmit sound. For example, *echo sounding* as a means of determining the depth of water is possible using sound waves. The fact that outside sounds can be heard inside a closed room is evidence of sound conduction through solids. Conduction of sound through bone may be used to aid people with impaired hearing.

Longitudinal waves

The word "longitudinal" means "running lengthwise". The force producing changes in air pressure by a sound wave is directed lengthwise, i.e. it acts along the direction of propagation. This type of wave is therefore referred to as a *longitudinal wave*.

1.7. Electromagnetic waves

When it is desired to extend the range of communications by means of line or radio, electromagnetic waves must be used. These can convey energy through empty space, and through some forms of matter, and can therefore give rise to an effect at a great distance from their source. By using a sound wave to control an electromagnetic wave as it is generated, the sound wave can be carried by the electromagnetic wave.

The nature of an electromagnetic wave is not as easily visualized as that of a sound wave because it is not so readily perceived by the senses. The wave consists of two types of forces, *electric force* and *magnetic force*, moving together in wave motion. These forces can only be detected by the effect they have on electric and magnetic charges. For example, a loop of wire suitably placed in a magnetic field which is varying with time, will have a current induced in it, and length of wire suitably positioned in an electric field will have a voltage produced across its ends. It is found that if an electric field of force is set into motion, it automatically sets up or generates a magnetic field of force, and if a magnetic field of force is set into motion it generates an electric field of force. In this manner an *electromagnetic* wave can be generated.

The electric field is usually denoted by the letter E and is measured in *volts per metre* (V/m). The magnetic field is measured in *amperes per metre* (A/m), and is denoted by H.

The fields are mutually at right angles and at right angles to the direction of motion. If the wave is sinusoidal, i.e. described by equations similar to those derived in § 1.5, the instantaneous values of electric and magnetic forces are given by

$$h = H_{max} \sin(2\pi ft),$$
$$e = E_{max} \sin(2\pi ft).$$

The velocity of an electromagnetic wave in free space is found to be approximately

$$v = 300 \times 10^6 \text{ m/s}.$$

This is also the velocity at which light travels in free space. It was this result (first derived by Clerk Maxwell, an English physicist, in 1865) which led to the *electromagnetic theory of light*.

Transverse electromagnetic waves

The word "transverse" means "acting in a crosswise direction". Both the electric field and the magnetic field act in a direction crosswise to the direction of motion, therefore this type of wave is referred to as a *transverse electromagnetic wave*, abbreviated TEM wave.

1.8. Polarization

The direction of the electric field relative to the surface of the earth determines the polarization of the electromagnetic wave. A *vertically polarized wave* is one in which the electric field is perpendicular to the earth's surface (i.e. vertical) and a *horizontally polarized wave* is one in which the electric field is parallel to the earth's surface (i.e. horizontal).

Both types of polarization are used in practice.

1.9. Electromagnetic transmission of sound

Sound energy can be converted into electromagnetic energy by means of a microphone. The question then arises—How to transmit this over large distances? Two practical solutions present themselves: (a) the use of line transmission, and (b) the use of radio. Concerning (b), all practical aerial systems have dimensions in the order of the wavelength being transmitted. A sound wave of 300 c/s converted into electromagnetic energy in space will have a wavelength of

$$\lambda = 3 \times 10^8/300 \text{ m}$$
$$= 10^6 \text{ m},$$

i.e. one million metres or about 625 miles. It is quite clear that an aerial system for this is impracticable.

The difficulty is overcome by using the low-frequency wave (termed the signal) to control some parameter of a very much higher frequency wave (termed the carrier). The carrier will always be a sine (or cosine) function of time, and therefore can be written as

$$A \sin (2\pi ft + \phi),$$

Two parameters are available for modulation; the amplitude A and the angle $(2\pi ft + \phi)$. Amplitude modulation is the subject of Chapter 4. Angle modulation will be treated in a separate volume.

1.10. Exercises

1. The velocity of sound in air at 0 °C is 332 m/s. Determine the wavelength of the following sound frequencies at 0 °C: (a) 100 c/s; (b) 300 c/s; (c) 10,000 c/s.

2. The velocity of sound in sea water is 1500 m/s and may be assumed constant at this value. Determine the wavelengths of the sound of Ex. 1 when transmitted through sea water. An echo-sounding equipment directs a supersonic wave directly downwards to the sea bed and receives an echo 60 msec later. Determine the depth of the sea at this point.

3. Explain the terms *frequency*, *wavelength*, *periodic time*, and *amplitude* as applied to wave propagation.

4. A radio wave is propagated through a block of polythene, in which its velocity of propagation is 2×10^8 m/s. If its wavelength is found to be 4 cm, what is the frequency of the wave? [C & G RLT A, 1960, part question.]

5. Draw a graph relating the free space wavelength to frequency for the medium wave broadcast band, the frequency limits of which are 500–1600 kc/s.

6. Determine the polarization of your nearest television network.

7. When the space satellite Mariner IV passed the planet Mars, it was 134,000,000 miles from Earth. The equipment on the satellite was controlled by a radio signal which sent an answering radio signal back to earth immediately the earth signal was received. Calculate the time lapse between sending a control signal from earth and knowing that this was revieved by the satellite.

CHAPTER 2

LOGARITHMIC UNITS

2.1. Introduction

Logarithmic units are used extensively in communications engineering. The underlying reason is that many of the calculations, and quantities involved, are best expressed as ratios. For example, the most convenient way of expressing the gain of a power amplifier is in terms of the *ratio* of output to input power. Noise is a limiting factor in many communications systems, and another important ratio is the *signal-to-noise ratio*.

When ratios are presented on linear graph paper the results tend to be misleading. This is because the eye measures off equal distances as being of equal value. Figure 2.1 shows how the signal-to-noise ratio varies for three different communications systems A, B and C. A first glance suggests that the signal-to-noise ratio for system A improves more rapidly than either B or C. Also that the difference between A and B is greater than that between B and C.

Closer examination of the curves and a little arithmetic shows that neither statement is true. The rate of improvement of signal-to-noise ratio is the same for all systems, namely they all increase by a factor of 1·69 for the range of input voltage shown. Also, system B is four times better than C whereas system A is only three times better than B. The fault lies in the graph which presents ratios (which are in effect multiplying factors) on a linear scale. The eye compares the length of one ordinate with another rather than their ratio, which is the relevant factor. An important function of any graph is that it should allow visual comparisons to be made easily and correctly. Figure 2.1 fails in this instance. The difficulty can be overcome by scaling the ordinate in numbers

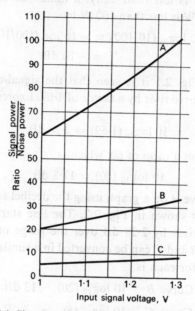

FIG. 2.1. Signal-to-noise power ratio vs. input voltage.

which are proportional to the logarithms of the ratios. Addition and subtraction of lengths of ordinates is then effectively the same as multiplying and dividing respectively the ratios which they represent.

2.2. The bel and the decibel

The most convenient practical unit based on logarithms is the *decibel*. The difference in decibels between two powers P_1 and P_2 is

$$10 \log_{10} \frac{P_1}{P_2}. \tag{2.1}$$

Thus 100 W is greater than 10 W by

$$10 \log_{10} (100/10) = 10 \text{ decibels (dB)}.$$

When the ratio is less than unity, a minus number of decibels result. Thus 10 W is less than 100 W by

$$10 \log_{10} (10/100) = -10 \log (100/10)$$
$$= -10 \text{ dB}.$$

Returning to Fig. 2.1 it is seen that the signal-to-noise power ratio for each curve rises by a factor of 1·69. Expressed in decibels this is:

$$10 \log_{10} (1\cdot69) = 2\cdot28 \text{ dB}.$$

Curve A starts at a ratio of 60, which is

$$10 \log_{10} (60) = 17\cdot8 \text{ dB}.$$

Redrawing curve A on a graph using the decibel scale results in a straight line as shown in Fig. 2.2. The line starts at the value 17·8 dB, and rises by 2·28 dB over the range of input voltage given. Curves B and C can be converted in a similar manner. The starting point for each is

Curve B $10 \log_{10} (20) = 13 \text{ dB}.$

Curve C $10 \log_{10} (5) = 7 \text{ dB}.$

Both rise by the same amount as A, namely 2·28 dB over the same range of input voltage.

All three curves are replotted in Fig. 2.2. It is apparent from this that they all rise at the same rate, and that system B represents a greater improvement over C than A over B.

The decibel is one-tenth of a larger unit known as the *bel*. The bel is the parent unit; the difference in *bels* between two powers P_1 and P_2 is

$$\log_{10} \frac{P_1}{P_2},$$

but this unit proved to be inconveniently large in practice.

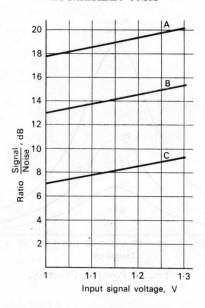

FIG. 2.2. Signal-to-noise ratio in decibels vs. input voltage (compare with Fig. 2.1).

2.3. Power gain and loss in decibels

Consider a radio-frequency power amplifier, the power gain of which varies with frequency as shown by curve A of Fig. 2.3. The power gain is the ratio of (power output)/(power input). The data for the curve is given in Table 2.1 along with the gain expressed in decibels.

TABLE 2.1. POWER GAIN VS. FREQUENCY. AMPLIFIER A

Frequency (Mc/s)	0·9	0·94	0·98	1·00	1·02	1·06	1·1
Power gain (ratio)	5·6	12·4	32	40	32	12·4	5·6
Power gain (dB)	7·5	11	15	16	15	11	7·5

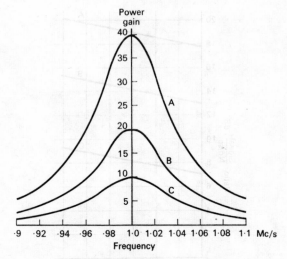

Fɪɢ. 2.3. Power vs. frequency.

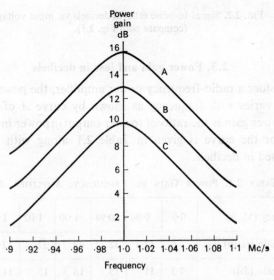

Fɪɢ. 2.4. Power gain in decibels vs. frequency (compare with Fig. 2.3).

Curves for two similar amplifiers *B* and *C* are also shown in Fig. 2.3. The three curves are replotted using a decibel scale (Fig. 2.4). Figure 2.4 shows that the change in gain with change in frequency is the same for each amplifier, and that the reduction in gain from *A* to *B* is equal to that from *B* to *C*. Neither point is directly apparent from Fig. 2.3.

When the gain of an amplifier drops below a ratio of unity it is said to have a loss. Consider amplifier *C* of the previous example connected to a radio-frequency transformer which passes only 50% of the power. The transformer has a power gain of 0·5 (i.e. a power loss) which in decibels is

$$10 \log_{10} (0·5) \text{ dB} = -3 \text{ dB}.$$

The overall gain of amplifier *C* plus transformer is shown in Fig. 2.5 for the same frequency range as before. It is assumed that the gain of the transformer does not change over the frequency range considered. The overall curve is obtained simply by substracting 3 dB from the curve for amplifier *C* alone.

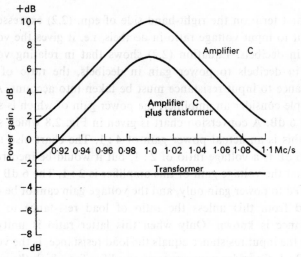

FIG. 2.5 Illustrating addition of gains using decibels.

2.4. Voltage and current ratios in decibels

The power input to an amplifier can be written as

$$P_i = V_i^2/R_i,$$

where P_i = power input, R_i = input resistance of amplifier, and V_i = voltage developed across R_i.

Likewise the output power can be written as

$$P = V^2/R_L,$$

where P = power into load resistance R_L, and V = voltage developed across R_L.

The gain of the amplifier in decibels is:

$$G\,(\text{dB}) = 10 \log_{10} \frac{P_L}{P_i}$$

$$= 10 \log_{10} \frac{V_L^2 R_i}{V_i^2 R_L}$$

$$= 20 \log_{10} \frac{V_L}{V_i} - 10 \log \frac{R_L}{R_i}. \qquad (2.2)$$

The first term on the right-hand side of eqn. (2.2) expresses the output to input voltage ratio in decibels, i.e. it gives the voltage gain in decibels. Equation (2.2) shows that in relating voltage gain in decibels to power gain in decibels, the ratio of load resistance to input resistance must be taken into account. As an example consider an amplifier, the power gain of which is stated to be 6 dB. A conversion chart is given in Fig. 2.8 which shows that this is an actual power gain of 4 : 1. The chart also shows that 6 dB is a voltage ratio of 2 : 1, but it would be incorrect to say that the voltage gain of this amplifier is 2 : 1. The 6 dB value referred to power gain only, and the voltage gain cannot be determined from this unless the ratio of load resistance to input resistance is known. Only when this latter ratio is unity, i.e. when the input resistance equals the load resistance, is the voltage gain 2 : 1. Consider now a second amplifier for which the *voltage gain* is stated as being 6 dB. Figure 2.8 shows that this represents an actual voltage gain 2 : 1. It would be incorrect to say that the power ratio was 4 : 1; again this condition only applies if the input resistance equals the load resistance. The decibel was defined originally in terms of a power ratio. The idea can now be extended to voltages. The difference (in decibels) between two voltages V_1 and V_2 is

$$20 \log \left(\frac{V_1}{V_2}\right). \qquad (2.3)$$

But, as shown, care must be taken when relating voltage gain to power gain, it then being necessary to know the ratio of resistances.

In a like manner, the powers P_i and P_L can be expressed in terms of the input and output currents thus:

$$P_i = I_i^2 R_i,$$
$$P_L = I_L^2 R_L.$$

The power gain in decibels is then

$$G\,(\text{dB}) = 10 \log_{10} \frac{I_L^2 R_L}{I_i^2 R_i}$$

$$= 20 \log_{10} \frac{I_L}{I_i} + 10 \log_{10} \frac{R_L}{R_i}. \qquad (2.4)$$

This equation is similar to eqn. (2.2), but the current ratio takes the place of the voltage ratio. Therefore the remarks concerning voltage ratios and decibels apply in full to current ratios and decibels. In particular, the difference (in decibels) between two currents I_1 and I_2 is

$$20 \log_{10} \frac{I_1}{I_2}. \qquad (2.5)$$

It will also be noted that the right-hand terms in eqn. (2.4) are added, not subtracted, as in eqn. (2.2). This will not alter the comparison in general.

2.5. Relative gains

Very often the gain of an amplifier relative to a particular fixed value is significant. An important characteristic of an amplifier is the manner in which its gain varies with frequency, relative to the maximum gain. This can be determined by subtracting the maximum gain (in decibels) from the gain (in decibels) at any frequency. This has been done for the amplifiers A, B and C of the previous example, and the result is shown in Fig. 2.6. It is seen

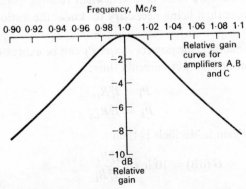

FIG. 2.6. Relative gain in decibels vs. frequency.

that the amplifiers have identical *relative gain/frequency* characteristics. From the curve, the relative gain at $1·07$ Mc/s is -6dB. This means that the output power has dropped to one-quarter of its 1 Mc/s value [see eqn. (2.1)]. Assuming that the load resistance R_L remains constant, it can also be said that the output voltage drops to one-half of its 1 Mc/s value.

Relative gain is always stated without reference to the kind of ratio involved on the assumption that the change in gain occurs across a constant resistance.

2.6. Absolute values in decibels

It is meaningless to state voltage, current or power in decibels. The decibel represents a ratio and must therefore involve two quantities. A power of 20 dB means nothing, but 20 dB relative to 1 W means 100 W. When, therefore, a quantity is stated in decibels the *reference value must also be stated.*

A useful extension to decibel is the dBm or decibels relative to one milliwatt. Thus 20 dBm is 100 mW, since 20 dB is a power ratio of 100 : 1. A similar idea can be applied to voltages and currents; for example dBV or $dB\mu V$, meaning respectively decibels relative to 1 V or to 1 μV.

The ability of a tuned circuit to select a wanted signal and to reject an unwanted signal is usually expressed in decibels. The reference level here is the level of the wanted signal. Thus a rejection of 60 dB means that the unwanted signal level is 60 dB below that of the wanted signal level. Since this is also a form of relative gain, 60 dB means that the unwanted voltage level is 10^{-3} times that of the wanted signal, or that the power is 10^{-6} times that of the wanted signal.

2.7. Decibel range

The use of decibels permits a very wide range of ratios to be shown on a linear scale. The chart of Fig. 2.7 illustrates this. The decibel range of 0–60 dB on a linear scale covers the enormous power ratio range of 1–1,000,000 and a voltage range of 1–1000. It would be quite impractible to show either of these on a linear scale. Because of the logarithmic nature of the ratio scales, compression occurs at each power of ten. This is seldom a disadvantage, the number of significant figures being the same at any part of the scale.

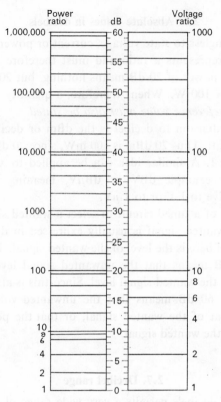

FIG. 2.7. Illustrating the wide range covered by the decibel scale.

2.8. Worked example

In this example and in the exercises that follow, the conversion chart of Fig. 2.8 may be used. Values outside the range of chart can be brought within range as explained in the example below.

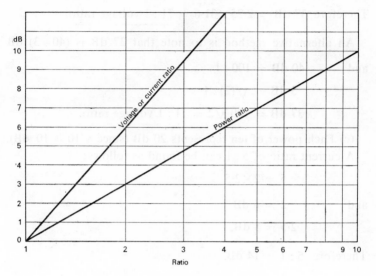

FIG. 2.8. Conversion chart for decibels.

EXAMPLE

Use the chart of Fig. 2.8 to convert:

(a) 16 decibels to a power ratio;
(b) 37 decibels to a voltage ratio;
(c) a current ratio of 500 : 1 to decibels.

(a) 16 decibels is $(10+6)$ dB.

$$10 \text{ dB} = 10 : 1 \text{ power ratio},$$
$$6 \text{ dB} = 4 : 1 \text{ power ratio}.$$

Therefore $\quad 16 \text{ dB} = (10 \times 4) : 1 \text{ power ratio}$
$$= 40 : 1 \text{ power ratio}.$$

(b) For voltage and current ratios it should be remembered that 10 dB represents a ratio of $\sqrt{(10)} : 1$.

$$30 \text{ dB} = \sqrt{10} \times \sqrt{10} \times \sqrt{10} = 31 \cdot 6 : 1,$$
$$7 \text{ dB} = 2 \cdot 25 : 1.$$

Therefore 37 dB = $2 \cdot 25 \times 31 \cdot 6 = \underline{71 : 1}$ voltage ratio.

An alternative method is to note that 37 dB is $(40-3)$ dB

and   40 dB = 100 : 1

3 dB = $\sqrt{(2)} : 1$

37 dB = $100/\sqrt{2} = \underline{71 : 1}$ voltage ratio.

(c) Each power of ten represents 20 dB (since $\sqrt{10}$ is 10 dB). A current ratio of 5 : 1 can be found as follows:

$$5 = 2 \times 2 \cdot 5$$

and   2 = 6 dB

$2 \cdot 5$ = 8 dB.

Therefore $5 : 1 = \underline{14 \text{ dB}}$.

Therefore   500 : 1 current ratio = $(14 + 20 + 20)$ dB

$$= \underline{54 \text{ dB}}.$$

Alternatively, the current ratio 500 : 1 = $(1000)/(2) : 1$

1000 : 1 = 60 dB

2 : 1 = 6 dB

500 : 1 = $60 - 6 = \underline{54 \text{ dB}}$.

Useful values to remember are:

Decibels	Voltage or current	Power ratio
	Ratio	
3	$\sqrt{2} : 1$	2 : 1
6	2 : 1	4 : 1
10	$\sqrt{10} : 1$	10 : 1
20	10 : 1	100 : 1

2.9. Exercises

1. (a) Express the following voltage ratios in decibels: 10 : 1; 250 : 1; 0·005 : 1.
   (b) Express the following current ratios in decibels: 2 : 1; 2·718 : 1; 0·01 : 1.
   (c) If the voltage used in determining the ratios in (a) were measured across the same resistor, determine the equivalent power ratios in decibels.

2. The signal-to-noise ratio of a communications system is 20 dB. If the signal power is increased by a factor of 5 : 1, the noise remaining unaltered, determine the new signal-to-noise ratio in decibels.

3. Explain why power cannot be expressed directly in decibels, and what is meant by the unit dBm.

The input power to a transmission line is 13 dBm. The line introduces an attenuation of 6 dB between input and output. Calculate:

   (a) the output power in dBm;
   (b) the output power in milliwatts;
   (c) the input power in milliwatts.

4. The maximum power input allowed to a certain transmission line is +30dBm. It is desired to supply the line from an amplifier delivering a maximum power of 2 W. Determine the attenuation necessary in amplifier gain.

5. The current in a resistor is increased by 21 dB, the resistance remaining constant. Determine (a) the increase, in decibels, in the voltage across the resistor, and (b) the increase in power in decibels, in the resistor.

CHAPTER 3

SPEECH AND MUSIC

3.1. Introduction

From the engineering point of view, speech and music belong to the same class of signals. They differ in transmission requirements in that music covers a greater frequency range and also a greater *dynamic* range (dynamic range is the range between maximum and minimum sound intensities).

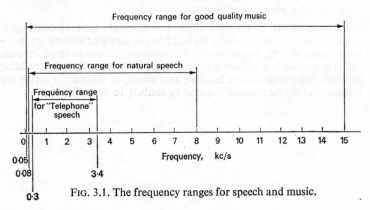

FIG. 3.1. The frequency ranges for speech and music.

The frequency ranges involved for each type of signal are shown in Fig. 3.1 and are discussed in the following sections. The *harmonic* composition of sound waves is also described.

3.2. Speech signals

Speech sounds are initiated by the passage of air between the *vocal cords*. The air causes the cords to vibrate, and the vibrations

28

in turn *modulate* (i.e. regulate) the air stream, thus producing sound. By suitably controlling the air stream and the muscular tension of the vocal cords, speech sounds can be formed.

The *vowel* sounds in a language are continuous sounds, and therefore result in *repetitive* type waves. Consonants introduce abrupt changes, i.e. they start and stop the vowel sounds and therefore introduce *impulse* type waves. Most languages are a combination of vowel and consonant sounds, and the sound waves are therefore complex. These can be broken down into sine (or cosine) waves, the number of which may be very great. The breaking-down process is known as *frequency analysis*, and plays an important part in communications engineering. Cavities such as the mouth amplify those frequencies at which they are resonant. Thus they have a profound effect on the final *sound* of the speech or what is referred to as the *timbre* of the voice.

3.3. Frequency analysis of speech

Figure 3.2 shows one cycle of the time curve for the sound *e* as in the word *eat*. By means of frequency analysis it can be

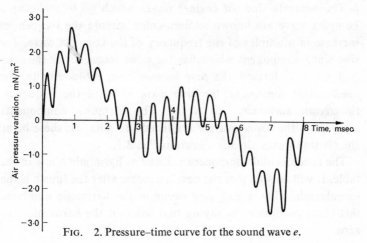

FIG. 2. Pressure–time curve for the sound wave *e*.

shown that this simple sound consists of six separate sine waves, and these are shown in Fig. 3.3. The actual frequency analysis is a complicated process and will not be carried out here, but the results can be checked by adding the ordinates of the six compo- nents waves shown in Fig. 3.3, when the resultant wave of Fig. 3.2 will be obtained. For example, if the ordinates at time 2 msec are taken, these are:

Wave	mN/m²
(a)	1·0
(b)	0
(c)	−0·35
(d)	0
(e)	0·25
(f)	−0·4
TOTAL	0·5

The total agrees with the value shown at time 2 msec in Fig 3.2.

The separate sine (or cosine) waves which go to make up a complex wave are known as *harmonics* because the frequencies increase in multiples of the frequency of the complex wave. The sine wave component which has the same frequency as the orig- inal wave is termed the *first harmonic* or, more usually, the *fundamental component;* the sine wave at twice the frequency, the *second harmonic*, and so on. The harmonic components making up the sound wave *e* are listed in Table 3.1, these being the six sine waves already shown in Fig. 3.3.

The fundamental component is listed as harmonic No. 1 in the table. It will be seen that the next harmonic after the fourth is the seventeenth. Thus a gap may occur in the harmonic numbers, this being equivalent to saying that some of the harmonics are zero.

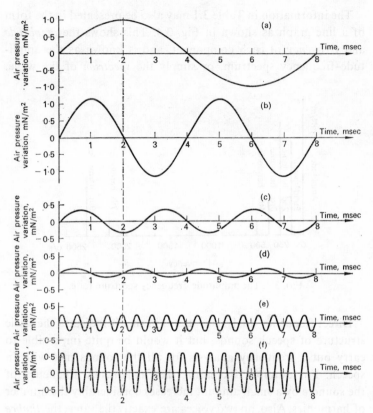

FIG. 3.3. The harmonic waves in *e*.

TABLE 3.1. HARMONIC WAVES IN THE SOUND WAVE FOR *e*

Harmonic No.	1	2	3	4	17	19
Frequency (c/s)	125	250	375	500	2125	2375
Amplitude (mN/m²)	1·0	1·17	0·334	0·125	0·25	0·58

(mN/m² = millinewtons per square metre. One mN = 100 dynes.)

The information in Table 3.1 may also be presented in the form of a line graph as shown in Fig. 3.4. This shows the *amplitude* and *frequency* of each component, and is known as the amplitude–frequency spectrum, or simply the *spectrum* of the wave.

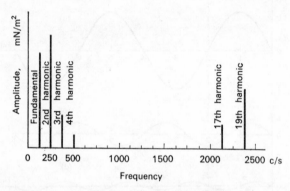

Fig. 3.4. The amplitude–frequency spectrum for *e*.

Direct frequency analysis is useful in that it indicates the basic structure of speech sounds, but it would be quite impossible to carry out a frequency analysis for all the sounds met with in speech. For example, increasing the fundamental frequency of the sound *e* by a small amount increases considerably the number of harmonics. Also, no two voices are exactly the same, the *timbre* or quality of the voice depending on the number of harmonics and their relative amplitudes.

Special tests have been devised (known as *articulation tests*) and as a result of these it is found that the *frequency bandwidth* required for speech is 300–3400 c/s. These frequency limits are not sharply defined, the figures being suitable values agreed upon internationally. In some applications, different limits may be used, but the 300–3400 c/s band is the normally accepted one for telephony (this is sometimes referred to as *commercial speech*). For broadcast entertainment, where high quality may be required, the speech band would be 80–8000 c/s, this being necessary to capture the naturalness of the speaker's voice.

It is worth noting that in normal speech the *energy* of the sounds is contained mostly in the low-frequency components while the clearness (or distinctness) of the speech depends on the high-frequency components.

3.4. Frequency range required for music

Music may be analysed into fundamental and harmonic waves in a similar manner to speech, and it is found that the frequency range covered is about 15–20,000 c/s. When music is reproduced (as, for example, by recordings or by radio) a much smaller range is satisfactory. Listening tests show that a range of about 160–8000 c/s is quite acceptable for normal single loud-speaker (or *monaural*) systems. With *stereophonic* systems, a somewhat wider bandwidth is desirable. Thus the bandwidth which is generally accepted as being satisfactory for reproducing music is 50–15 000 c/s, as this allows for stereophonic reproduction, and for the views of *high fidelity* enthusiasts.

3.5. Exercises

1. Explain what is meant by the *fundamental* and the *harmonics* of a sound wave. A complex sound wave has a frequency of 250 c/s and consists of a fundamental component, a third and a fifth harmonic. What are the frequencies of these components?

2. In the amplitude–spectrum of Fig. 3.4, assuming that the nineteenth harmonic is the highest present in the wave, state the harmonics which have zero amplitude.

3. A musical note is found to have a periodic time of 5 msec, and consists of a fundamental and harmonics up to the third. Calculate the frequencies in the spectrum.

CHAPTER 4

AMPLITUDE MODULATION

4.1. Introduction

To modulate means to regulate or adjust. Modulation fulfils three important functions in a communications system:

(a) The conversion of information into an electrical signal.
(b) It makes possible *radio transmission* of information.
(c) It provides a means of sending many channels of information over one communications link, this being known as *multiplexing*.

Amplitude modulation was the first method to be developed and is used extensively today in radio and line transmission. Another form is *angle modulation* and this will be treated in a further volume.

4.2. Amplitude modulation

An example of a simple amplitude modulation system is the fuel-level indicator system used in most cars. The fuel level (the information) regulates the amplitude of an electrical current which is then transmitted to an indicator on the front panel. The current is said to "carry" the information and is therefore referred to as the *carrier*. Another, similar example, is where a sound wave regulates a current through a carbon microphone. These are both examples of function (a).

When functions (b) and (c) are being provided, the carrier is a high-frequency sinusoidal wave (known as the *carrier wave*).

The electrical signal representing speech or music is used to control this (modulation circuits are described in a later volume), and, for practical reasons, the frequency of the highest harmonic in the speech or music signal must be considerably less than the frequency of the carrier. Also, the amplitude of the speech or music signal (the modulating signal) must never be greater than the carrier amplitude.

In the most general form of amplitude modulation the modulating signal is *added* to the *amplitude* of the carrier. The carrier may be represented by a sine wave, as shown in Fig. 4.1(a) for

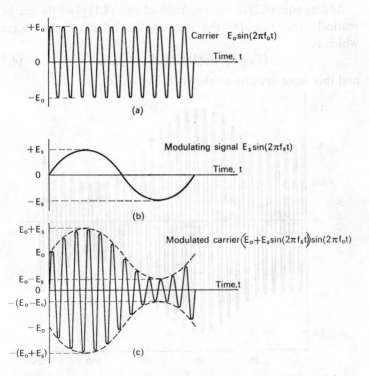

FIG. 4.1. (a) An unmodulated carrier wave. (b) A sinusoidal modulating signal. (c) The resulting modulated wave.

which the corresponding mathematical expression is

$$E_0 \sin (2\pi f_0 t), \tag{4.1}$$

where E_0 is the carrier amplitude (or peak value) and f_0 is the carrier frequency.

Let the modulating signal also be represented by a sine wave, as shown in Fig. 4.1(b), and for which the mathematical expression is

$$E_s \sin (2\pi f_s t), \tag{4.2}$$

where E_s is the amplitude (or peak value of the signal) and f_s is the frequency of the signal.

Adding eqn. (4.2) to the *amplitude* of eqn. (4.1) gives the mathematical expression for the resulting modulated carrier wave, which is

$$[E_0 + E_s \sin (2\pi f_s t)] \sin (2\pi f_0 t), \tag{4.3}$$

and this wave appears as shown in Fig. 4.1(c).

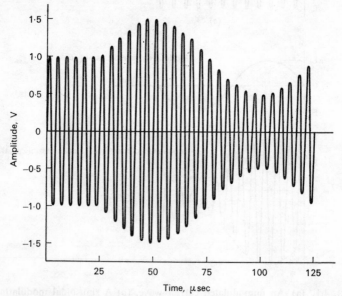

Fig. 4 2. A 240 kc/s, 1·0 V carrier modulated by a 10 kc/s, 0·5 V sine wave.

Figure 4.2 shows an example of a carrier wave modulated by a sine wave for which the carrier has an amplitude E_0 of 1·0 V, and a frequency f_0 of 240 kc/s, and the sinusoidal modulating wave an amplitude E_s of 0·5 V and a frequency f_s of 10 kc/s. The carrier is shown unmodulated for the first 25 μ sec.

4.3. Frequencies in a modulated wave

When a carrier is modulated by a sine wave, only two frequencies are involved—that of the carrier and that of the modulating wave. Frequency analysis of the resultant wave [given by eqn. (4.3)] shows that the *modulated wave* is made up of *three* separate sinusoidal waves, the frequencies of which are

(i) f_0,

(ii) f_0+f_s,

(iii) f_0-f_s.

The first frequency is obviously the *carrier frequency*. The second frequency is termed the *upper side frequency* because it appears beside the carrier but above it, and the third frequency is termed the *lower side frequency*.

The mathematical expression for the modulated wave can also be analysed into three terms representing the carrier and the two side frequencies, and these are found to be:

Carrier $\qquad\qquad\qquad E_0 \sin\ (2\pi f_0 t)$

Upper side frequency $\quad \frac{1}{2}E_s \cos 2\pi(f_0+f_s)t$

Lower side frequency $\quad \frac{1}{2}E_s \cos 2\pi(f_0-f_s)t$

These three components may be presented as an amplitude–frequency spectrum, and Fig. 4.3 shows the spectrum for the modulated wave of Fig. 4.2. The three waves given by the above expressions are shown in Fig. 4.4, and these may be added to-

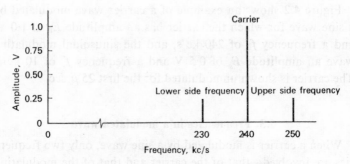

FIG. 4.3. The spectrum graph for the wave of Fig. 4.2.

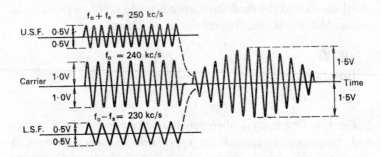

FIG. 4.4. The carrier and side frequencies for the wave of Fig. 4.2.

gether to give the modulated wave of Fig. 4.2. The addition process is similar to that already described in connection with Fig. 3.3.

4.4. Carrier modulated with speech or music

It has already been shown that speech and music signals consist of a number of waves (fundamentals and their harmonics). When modulation takes place, each component wave produces its own upper and lower side frequency, and thus for speech or music there will be a number of upper side frequencies and a number of lower side frequencies. These are referred to collectively as the *upper sideband* and the *lower sideband*. Figure 4.5(a) shows a carrier wave amplitude-modulated with the speech sound *e* (which was analysed in § 3.3), and Fig. 4.5(b) shows the spectrum with the upper and lower sidebands.

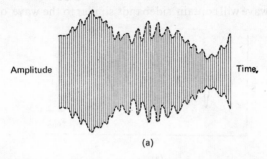

Amplitude   Time.

(a)

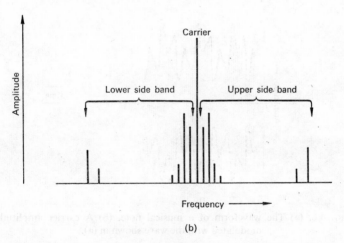

(b)

FIG. 4.5. (a) A carrier amplitude-modulated with speech. (b) The spectrum for (a).

With a musical note the harmonics depend very much on the type of instrument and on how it is played. For example, a French horn can produce a note which is a sine wave, and the amplitude-modulated wave would appear similar to that of Fig. 4.2. The clarinet can produce a note, the waveform of which is as shown in Fig. 4.6(a), and the resulting amplitude-modulated wave in this case will be as shown in Fig. 4.6(b). The spectrum for this wave will contain sidebands similar to the wave of Fig. 4.5.

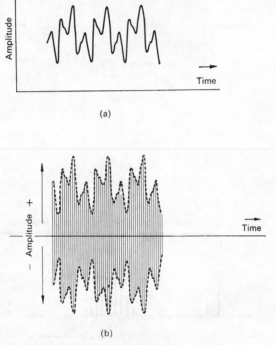

(a)

(b)

FIG. 4.6. (a) The waveform of a musical note. (b) A carrier amplitude-modulated with the wave shown in (a).

4.5. Modulation index and modulation depth

In amplitude modulation it is important that the signal amplitude E_s should never exceed the carrier amplitude E_0. The most convenient way of keeping a check on this is to work in terms of the ratio E_s/E_0. This ratio is termed the *modulation index* and is denoted by m; m must never exceed unity and, in fact, it must always be within the range zero to unity. Expressed mathematically,

$$0 \leqslant m \leqslant 1.$$

Figure 4.7 shows modulated waves for three different values of m. It is clear that for a modulation index greater than unity ($m > 1$) distortion occurs, the negative peaks of the modulating signal being clipped. This is undesirable in itself, but it is harmful in another way. Distortion of this kind produces high-order

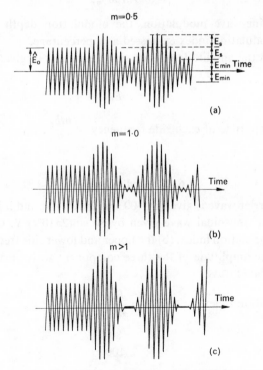

FIG. 4.7. Illustrating the meaning of modulation index.

side frequencies which interfere with adjacent channels (interference known as "sideband splash").

Modulation depth is the peak downward change in amplitude expressed as percentage of the carrier amplitude. From Fig. 4.7(a)

$$\text{modulation depth} = \frac{E_0 - E_{min}}{E_0} \times 100\%.$$

But for sine-wave modulation, $E_0 - E_{min} = E_s$.
This is shown on Fig. 4.7(a).

Hence, modulation depth $= (E_s/E_0) \times 100\%$

$$= m \times 100\%,$$

or, for sine-wave modulation, the modulation depth is equal to the modulation index expressed as a percentage.

In § 4.3 the amplitude of each side frequency is given as $\frac{1}{2}E_s$. Now,

$$E_s = mE_0.$$

Hence amplitude of each side frequency $= \dfrac{mE_0}{2}$.

4.6. Worked examples

1. A carrier wave is given by $100 \sin(2\pi 10^6 t)$ V, and it is modulated by a sinusoidal wave given by $80 \sin(2\pi 10^3 t)$ V. Calculate (a) the modulation index, (b) the upper and lower side frequencies, and (c) the amplitude of the three component waves making up the modulated wave.

Modulation index $\qquad m = \dfrac{E_s}{E_0}$

$$= \frac{80}{100}$$

$$= \underline{0 \cdot 8}.$$

The carrier frequency is 10^6 c/s, and the modulating frequency is 10^3 c/s. Hence,

Upper side frequency $= 1\cdot0$ Mc/s$+0\cdot001$ Mc/s
$= 1\cdot001$ Mc/s.

Lower side frequency $= 1\cdot0$ Mc/s$—0\cdot001$ Mc/s
$= 0\cdot999$ Mc/s.

The carrier amplitude remains unchanged and is 100 V.
The amplitude of each side frequency is $\frac{1}{2}\times80 = 40$ V.

2. A 60 kc/s carrier is amplitude-modulated by a speech signal containing frequencies up to 3400 c/s. Determine the lowest and the highest frequencies in the modulated signal.

Lowest frequency $\quad= 60-3\cdot4$
$= 56\cdot6$ kc/s.

Highest frequency $\quad= 60+3\cdot4$
$= 63\cdot4$ kc/s.

3. With reference to an amplitude-modulated wave what is meant by *sidebands?*

Why do medium-wave broadcast receivers, used for the reception of amplitude-modulated signals, require a total bandwidth of 9 kc/s?

Briefly describe effects on the reception of a medium-wave broadcast signal if the total bandwidth of the receiver were made (a) much less than, and (b) much greater than, 9 kc/s. [C & G RLT A, 1962.]

Answer. The meaning of sidebands is given in § 4.4. Receivers have a bandwidth of approximately 9 kc/s in order to accommodate both sidebands transmitted with carrier in this class of service. The extent of the sidebands is determined primarily by the nature of the modulating signal, which in this case includes speech and music signals. The sidebands must not be allowed to extend too far otherwise they overlap into the spectrum of neighbouring transmissions, causing interference. Ideally, each sideband for this class of modulating signal should be at least 15 kc/s, requiring a total receiver bandwidth of 15 by 2 or 30 kc/s. Because the medium wave band is overcrowded with transmissions, the bandwidth is limited (by international agreement) to much less than the ideal to prevent mutual interference. In practice the figure is 9 kc/s total, thus limiting each sideband to 4·5 kc/s. Reducing the receiver bandwidth would cut the high-frequency components in the modulating signal. The effect aurally would be much the same as setting the "tone control" to the "bass boost" position. Increasing the bandwidth of the receiver would not improve the quality of the output since the transmitted bandwidth is restricted. The increased bandwidth would make the receiver liable to a great deal of interference, especially at night-time when distant transmissions are easily received.

4.7. Exercises

1. Sketch the waveforms of a radio-frequency carrier wave, amplitude-modulated by a sine-wave tone, when the depth of modulation is (a) 100%, and (b) 25%.

If a radio frequency carrier wave is amplitude-modulated by a band of speech frequencies 50–4500 c/s, what will be the bandwidth of the transmission and what frequencies will be present in the transmitted wave if the carrier frequency is 506 kc/s? [C & G RLT A, 1959.]

2. With reference to an amplitude-modulated wave, explain what is meant by the term *modulation index*. A carrier wave of amplitude 1·0 V is amplitude-modulated by sinusoidal voltage of amplitude 0·3 V. Calculate (a) the modulation depth, and (b) the amplitude of the side frequencies.

3. The spectrum for an amplitude-modulated wave is found to contain the following components:

Amplitude (V)	Frequency (kc/s)
50	110
200	100
50	90

Determine from these (a) the carrier frequency, (b) the modulating frequency, and (c) the modulation depth.

4. A carrier wave of amplitude 10 V and frequency 50 kc/s is amplitude-modulated by a speech signal consisting of a fundamental of 1·0 V amplitude and frequency 1000 c/s and a second harmonic of amplitude 0·1 V. Calculate the amplitude and frequency of each component wave making up the modulated wave, and draw the amplitude–frequency spectrum.

CHAPTER 5

PASSIVE COMPONENTS

5.1. Introduction

The term *passive* refers to components which do not, in themselves, generate electricity. Although in a very strict sense any component generates electricity which appears as noise, this is

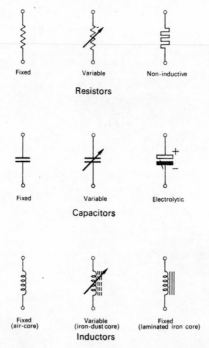

FIG. 5.1. Symbols for resistance, inductance and capacitance.

usually discounted in the definition of passive components. Three fundamental properties are associated with passive components:

(a) Resistance,
(b) Capacitance,
(c) Inductance.

It is impossible in practice to obtain any one of these properties at the exclusion of the others, but good component design aims at minimizing unwanted properties. The symbolic representation for each property is shown in Fig. 5.1.

5.2. Resistance

The characteristic which distinguishes resistance from all other circuit properties is that *voltage and current are always exactly in phase* with each other. Being in phase means that the time curves for voltage and current vary exactly together.

The resistance of a conductor is found to be proportional to the length of the conductor, and inversely proportional to its cross-sectional area. Let the uniform cross-sectional area be A m^2 and the length be l m, then the resistance can be written as

$$R = \frac{\varrho l}{A},$$

where ϱ is a constant termed the *resistivity* of the material making up the conductor. This depends on the atomic structure of the material and must be found by experiment. It also depends on temperature.

Conductivity is simply the reciprocal of resistivity. It is denoted by σ and

$$\sigma = \frac{1}{\varrho}.$$

It follows that the *conductance* of a material is the reciprocal of the resistance. Conductance is denoted by G, and

$$G = \frac{1}{R}.$$

TABLE 5.1. ELECTRICAL PROPERTIES OF CONDUCTORS

ϱ = resistivity Ω-m at 20 °C
σ = conductivity $\mho$/m at 20 °C

Material	ϱ	σ
Silver, annealed	$1\cdot58\times10^{-8}$	$0\cdot634\times10^{8}$
Copper, annealed	$1\cdot72\times10^{-8}$	$0\cdot58\ \times10^{8}$
Aluminium, hard-drawn	$2\cdot8\ \times10^{-8}$	$0\cdot357\times10^{8}$
Carbon, graphitic	$4600\ \ \times10^{-8}$	$0\cdot213\times10^{6}$
Constantan (alloy)	$48\ \ \times10^{-8}$	$0\cdot208\times10^{8}$

Applications. Silver is used largely for contacts in switches and relays when very low contact resistance is required. Copper is used universally as an electrical conductor and may also be used in alloy form for contacts. Aluminium is not entirely suitable as a wire conductor, but finds wide application as a chassis material. Carbon is an extremely useful material for specialized applications, such as the manufacture of valve anodes, brushes for electrical machines, the manufacture of resistors, and the carbon microphone.

Constantan is a metal alloy used mainly in the construction of precision resistors.

The unit of resistance is the ohm (Ω) named after G. S. Ohm, a German physicist. Commonly used multiples are the kilohm (kΩ), 10^3 ohms, and the megohm (MΩ), 10^6 ohms. Submultiples are the milli-ohm (10^{-3} ohms) and the microhm (10^{-6} ohms).

5.3. Construction of resistor

The composition type resistor is the commonest type encountered in telecommunications equipment. The basic raw materials used are *carbon black,* which is the resistive ingredient, *a resin binder*, and a refractory filling, which strengthens the resistor against the effects of heat and corrosion. The materials are combined in the required proportions and then baked in an oven at temperatures not exceeding 800 °F.

The basic resistor element is then as shown in Fig. 5.2(a). Insulation may be added if desired, and a ceramic insulated resistor is shown in Fig. 5.2(b).

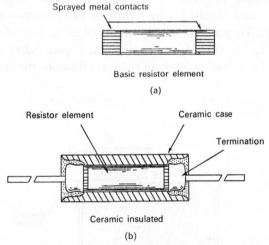

Sprayed metal contacts

Basic resistor element

(a)

Resistor element   Ceramic case

Termination

Ceramic insulated

(b)

FIG. 5.2. Carbon resistor construction.
(Courtesy Erie Resistor Ltd.)

Carbon resistors are satisfactory for the majority of circuit applications. They have the advantage of (a) being inexpensive, (b) having low stray inductance and capacitance and are therefore useful at high frequencies, and (c) are easily obtained in a wide range of resistance values, from a few ohms to many megohms.

The chief limitations are (a) power ratings are limited to several watts at the maximum, otherwise they become bulky; (b) they are not precision components, the resistance tending to change with time, and to change with applied voltage when the latter is large; (c) they have a large negative temperature coefficient of resistance, and (d) they tend to be noisier than comparable wire-wound types.

The degree of control in the manufacture of wire-wound resistors is much greater than that possible for carbon types. Thus precision resistors, such as used in instrument shunts, are wire-wound. The resistance can be made independent of temperature by using resistance wire such as constantan.

Wire-wound resistors can be made to handle large powers (up to several hundred watts) without being excessively large physically. They are commonly employed as "voltage dropping" resistors in communications equipment. Figure 5.3(a) shows a typical wire-wound resistor. In some applications the inductance

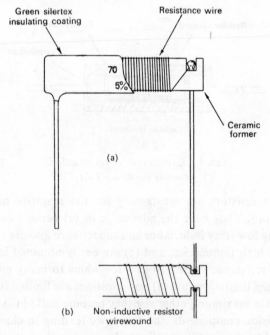

(a)

(b)   Non-inductive resistor wirewound

FIG. 5.3. Wire-wound resistor construction.

((a) Courtesy Erie Resistor Ltd.)

of the winding must be reduced to a negligible value. This can be achieved by winding the wire back upon itself as shown in Fig. 5.3(b). The adjacent wires carry the same current, but flowing in opposite directions, therefore the magnetic fields due to these cancel each other.

Alloys commonly used in the manufacture of wire-wound resistors are nickel–chromium and copper–chromium. The former has the higher resistivity and the lower temperature coefficient of resistance of the two.

Variable resistors may also be made of carbon or wire. Figure

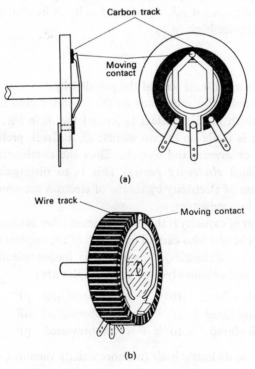

(a)

(b)

FIG. 5.4. Variable resistor construction.

5.4(a) shows a carbon type and Fig. 5.4(b) a wire-wound type. Generally, the carbon type come in medium to high-resistance values, such as are used for volume controls of radio receivers, while the wire-wound types are low to medium resistance and have a higher power dissipation than the carbon type and have a better control of resistance–rotation. The law of resistance against rotation can be made to almost any desired shape in both types.

5.4. Capacitance

Capacitance describes the ability of a passive system to hold electricity. For a simple capacitor consisting of two flat parallel metal plates, area A m², separated d m by an insulating material, the capacitance is given by

$$C = \frac{\varepsilon A}{d},$$

where ε is a constant termed the **permittivity**.

The permittivity ε depends on the insulator used between the plates, which in this context is termed the *dielectric*. The word dielectric is made up of two words; di, a Greek prefix meaning *through*, or *across*, and electric. Thus the combination means *across which electricity passes*. This is to distinguish it from conduction of electricity by means of electron movement such as happens in conductors.

The unit of capacity is the *Farad* (named after Michael Faraday, a British chemist who carried out much of the original experimental work on dielectrics). The Farad is inconveniently large in practice, and commonly used submultiples are:

The microfarad	10^{-6}	F	abbreviated	μF
The nanofarad	10^{-9}	F	abbreviated	nF
The picofarad	10^{-12}	F	abbreviated	pF

When the dielectric is air (or more strictly vacuum), the permittivity is given a special symbol ε_0, known as the *permittivity of free space*. It can be shown that the value of ε_0 in the rationalized m.k.s. system of units is

$$\varepsilon_0 = \frac{1}{36\pi 10^{12}} \, .$$

Relative permittivity (or *dielectric constant*). Most dielectrics have a permittivity greater that of free space, and therefore they increase the capacitance of a system over its free-space value. The ratio of the dielectric permittivity to the permittivity of free space is known as the *relative permittivity* and it is given the symbol ε_r. Thus

$$\varepsilon_r = \frac{\varepsilon}{\varepsilon_0} \quad \text{or} \quad \varepsilon = \varepsilon_r \varepsilon_0 \, .$$

It will be seen that the relative permittivity also gives the factor by which the capacity of the system is increased over its free space value. It is a very important factor in the design of capacitors, and some typical values are listed in Table 5.2.

TABLE 5.2. TYPICAL RELATIVE
PERMITTIVITIES OF SOME
DIELECTRIC MATERIALS

Material	ε_r
Vacuum	1·0
Air	1·0006
Mica	6·0
Paper	3·0
Ceramic	10·0
Special "Hi K" ceramic	1000

When the voltage across a capacitor is sinusoidal it is found that the current through it is cosinusoidal, i.e. the current–time curve is a cosine wave. Thus, a characteristic which distinguishes capacitance from all other circuit properties is that *for sinusoidal waveforms the current through the capacitor leads the voltage by exactly 90°.*

5.5. Construction of capacitors

Ceramic is one of the most suitable dielectric materials for radio-frequency capacitors. At these frequencies, capacitance values in general use range from a few picofarads to tens of

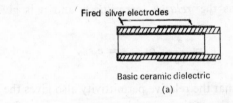

Fired silver electrodes

Basic ceramic dielectric

(a)

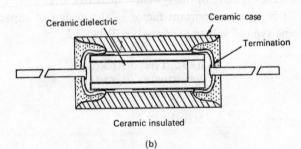

Ceramic dielectric

Ceramic case

Termination

Ceramic insulated

(b)

FIG. 5.5. Capacitor construction; suitable for high frequencies.
(Courtesy Erie Resistor Ltd.)

thousands of picofarads. These can be simply constructed on ceramic such that lead-inductance and other stray reactances are negligible. Figure 5.5 shows the constructional features of one type of ceramic capacitor.

At lower frequencies (e.g. audio frequencies), higher capacitance values are generally encountered (typically 0·05–0·1 μF). The "rolled" form of construction is employed using a paper or a plastic-film dielectric. Paper has the advantage of being cheap. In the rolled form (Fig 5.6), two layers of paper are required. This is because it is impossible to remove all conducting particles from the paper, but the chance of two conducting regions coming opposite each other in the double dielectric is slight.

As an alternative to paper, a single, very thin layer of plastic film may be used. This considerably reduces the physical size of the capacitor, but at a corresponding large increase in price. Suitable plastics are polystyrene and terylene (mylar in the U.S.A.).

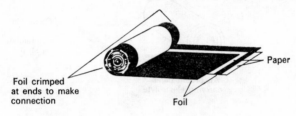

Foil crimped
at ends to make
connection

Paper

Foil

FIG. 5.6. Paper-foil capacitor; suitable for low frequencies.

Electrolytic-type capacitors employ some form of oxide coating as a dielectric, usually aluminium oxide. This has a high relative permittivity and can be made extremely thin without showing electrical breakdown. For the normal type, see Fig. 5.7(a), the polarity of voltage is important, as reverse voltage destroys the oxide film. Reversible types are also manufactured in which two oxide films are present as shown in Fig. 5.7(b).

Electrolytic capacitors may be constructed in rolled form as shown in Fig. 5.7(c). Typical capacitance values range from 10 to 40 μF, and they are used mainly in the smoothing circuits of power supplies and as decoupling capacitors.

Air dielectric variable capacitors are used as tuning capacitors in receivers and transmitters. Figure 5.8 illustrates a four-gang (i.e. a four-section) tunable capacitor, used in communication receivers. In domestic receivers, two-gang versions are normally used.

The movable vanes are carried on the spindle and are normally connected to earth through the framework. This reduces hand-capacity effects when tuning. Often a metallic spring contact is

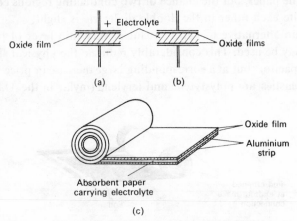

FIG. 5.7. Electrolytic capacitor construction.

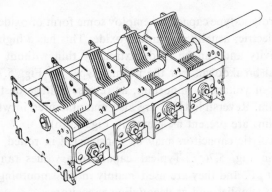

FIG. 5.8. A variable capacitor. (Up to 603 pF per section.)

provided onto the spindle. The fixed vanes are insulated from the framework by means of ceramic mountings.

The variation of capacity with rotation can be made to follow almost any desired law by specially shaping the capacitor plates.

However, in domestic receivers all sections are made identical to reduce cost.

Preset variable, or trimmer capacitors, allow small adjustments to be made in capacity values. Two types are illustrated in Fig. 5.9.

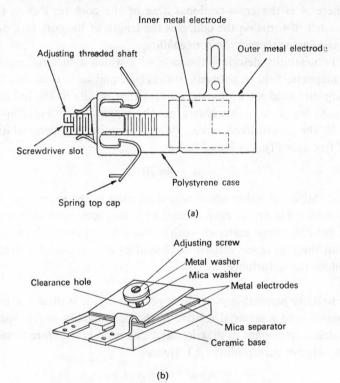

(a)

(b)

FIG. 5.9. Trimmer capacitors.
((a) Courtesy Erie Resistor Ltd.)

5.6. Inductance

The term *inductance* is used in connection with the fact that a current which varies with time can *induce* electromotive forces (e.m.f.s) both in the conductor carrying the current and in any neighbouring conductors. The inductance of a coil is given by:

$$L = \frac{\mu A N^2}{d},$$

where A is the cross-sectional area of the core (m²), N is the number of turns on the coil, d is the length of the core (m), and μ is a factor termed the *permeability*.

Permeability describes the ease with which a material allows a magnetic field to *permeate* through it, and as it is in fact the magnetic field set up by the current that results in the induced e.m.f., the permeability enters into the expression for inductance.

In the rationalized m.k.s. system of units, the permeability of free space (μ_0) is found to be

$$\mu_0 = 4\pi \, 10^{-7},$$

and this is the value which would be used in the expression for inductance if an air core instead of a magnetic core were used in the coil. Some materials such as brass have permeabilities less than the free space value and, if used as core material, actually reduce the inductance.

Relative permeability. As with permittivity, it is often the permeability of a material relative to the permeability of free space which is important in practice, and this ratio is therefore termed the relative permeability (μ_r). Hence

$$\mu_r = \mu/\mu_0 \quad \text{or} \quad \mu = \mu_0 \, \mu_r$$

The relative permeability is not a constant but varies with the magnetic flux density in the material. Some typical values are listed in Table 5.3.

When a sinusoidal current is passed through an inductance, it is found that the induced voltage is cosinusoidal, i.e. the voltage–time curve is a cosine wave. Thus, a characteristic which distinguishes inductance from all other circuit properties is that

TABLE 5.3. TYPICAL VALUES FOR
RELATIVE PERMEABILITIES OF SOME
COMMON MAGNETIC MATERIALS

Material	Range of μ_r
Iron	250– 5000
Silicon steel	400– 9000
Permalloy B	2000– 20,000
Mumetal	10,000–100,000

for sinusoidal waveforms the voltage leads the current by exactly 90°.

This should be compared with the corresponding characteristic for capacitance.

The unit of inductance is the henry (H), named after J. Henry, an American physicist. Commonly used submultiples are the millihenry (mH) or 10^{-3} H, and the microhenry (μH) or 10^{-6} H. Inductances in large multiples of the henry are not encountered in practice.

5.7. Construction of inductors

For most radio-frequency applications inductors can be simply constructed, Fig. 5.10 showing two commonly used types. The self-supporting coil shown in Fig 5.10(a) may be made out of

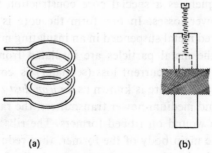

(a)   (b)

FIG. 5.10. Radio-frequency inductors.

stiff wire, and is useful at high frequencies, e.g. 100 Mc/s. In some instances the wire may be silver-plated, since at very high frequencies the current flows close to the surface of the wire (this is known as the *skin effect*). Where a larger value of inductance is required than can conveniently be constructed as a self-supporting coil, a coil-former is used to support the greater number of turns, and the wire is usually thin enamel-covered. The former may be made out of paxolin, ceramic or other insulating material.

At frequencies of the order a few megacycles per second, a multilayer inductance is usually required. The self-capacitance must be kept small by employing special winding techniques, a *wave winding* being an example of this. In this, the winding zigzags across the width, so that air spaces are introduced between layers, and the turns are well spaced. This also reduces the inductance, and is the price paid for reducing self-capacitance. A wave-wound coil is shown in Fig. 5.10(b). This is a tunable coil having an adjustable magnetic core.

At these frequencies the skin effect is also important, as the crowding of current to the surface of the wire effectively increases the resistance. A special stranded wire, known as *litzendraht (litz wire* for short), is then used, which prevents a large increase in resistance taking place.

It may also be necessary to use magnetic cores at radio-frequencies [one use being for tuning as shown in Fig. 5.10(b)]. At these frequencies a special core construction must be used to reduce power losses. In one form the core is made out of finely powdered metal suspended in an insulating material in such a way that the metal particles are insulated from each other. In this way the eddy-current loss (see later) is considerably reduced. This type of core is known as *an iron-dust core*.

For low- and medium-power transmitters, the radio-frequency inductors are wound on ribbed formers. The ribs keep the wire clear from the main body of the former, thus reducing dielectric losses. The wire itself may be hollow, i.e. in the form of a tube, again because the currents at radio-frequencies tend to crowd towards the surface of the wire and therefore the centre of the wire carries little current.

The inductors discussed so far have values ranging from a few microhenrys to many millihenrys. At low frequencies, e.g. audio frequencies, much larger values of inductance are encountered, and this generally means that magnetic cores are required. The

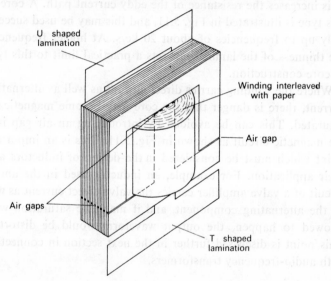

U shaped
lamination

Winding interleaved
with paper

Air gap

Air gaps

T shaped
lamination

FIG. 5.11. A low-frequency inductor.

core material fulfils the function of increasing the flux density within the winding and therefore should have large relative permeability. At the same time, the losses induced in the core must be kept small. These losses arise in two ways: *hysteresis loss* and *eddy-current loss*. The former is determined by the internal structure of the core material and will not be discussed here. Eddy currents are currents which are induced in the core by transformer action. The core offers resistance to these, and thus heat is generated. By increasing the resistance of the core the eddy currents are reduced and the overall result is a reduction in the power loss. A number of methods are commonly used for increasing the resistance. The core material may be a compound of silicon steel, which has a higher resistance than normal steel. In addition to this, the core may be laminated, i.e. constructed from very thin sections, these being insulated from each other. This increases the resistance of the eddy current path. A core of this type is illustrated in Fig. 5.11, and this may be used successfully up to frequencies of about 20 kc/s. At higher frequencies the thinness of the laminations sets a practical limit to this type of core construction.

Where the winding carries direct current as well as alternating current, there is danger that the core may become magnetically saturated. This can be avoided by introducing an air gap into the magnetic circuit as shown in Fig. 5.11. This is an important point which must be considered in the design of inductors and their application. For example, an inductor used in the anode circuit of a valve amplifier carries the valve direct current as well as the alternating component, and if magnetic saturation were allowed to happen, the output waveform would be distorted. This point is discussed further in the next section in connection with audio-frequency transformers.

5.8. Mutual inductance and transformers

The magnetic field set up by an alternating current is also capable of inducing an e.m.f. in any neighbouring circuit, and this is the underlying principle of the transformer. The winding to which the alternating-current supply is connected is termed the *primary*, and the other windings are termed the *secondary* windings. A transformer may have more than one secondary winding, and Fig. 5.12(a) shows the circuit symbol for a transformer with two secondaries. The physical construction of such a transformer used for low frequency (e.g. 50 c/s power supply frequency) is shown in Fig. 5.12(b). The core for this type of transformer is laminated in the same way as the low-frequency inductor and for the same reason. Since the windings are unlikely to carry direct current and since distortion is not a problem in power transformers, the air gaps in the core are staggered to provide a good magnetic circuit.

When the transformer is used for audio frequencies in amplifier circuits, there is danger of magnetic saturation, and the air

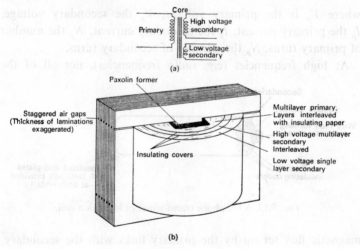

FIG. 5.12. A power transformer.

gaps must be in line to prevent a high flux density occurring. Distortion of audio-frequency currents must, of course, be avoided. For this reason, too, the core material for audio-frequency transformers is of much higher quality compared with that for power transformers.

A type of audio transformer extensively used in telephone circuits (see § 13.2) is shown in Fig. 5.13. This is known as an *induction coil*. The core consists simply of wire rods, and forms an *open magnetic circuit*. This means that the iron forms only part of the magnetic circuit, the rest being completed through air, and so there is no danger of magnetic saturation. Furthermore, variations in the permeability of the iron have only a very small effect on the complete magnetic circuit, and this also prevents distortion of the speech signals.

For low-frequency transformers the following relationships can be shown to hold *approximately* true:

$$V_p/V_s = N_p/N_s \quad \text{and} \quad I_p/I_s = N_s/N_p,$$

where V_p is the primary voltage, V_s the secondary voltage, I_p the primary current, I_s the secondary current, N_p the number of primary turns, N_p the number of secondary turns.

At high frequencies (e.g. radio frequencies), not all of the

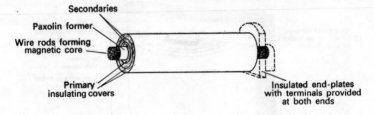

FIG. 5.13. A telephone transformer or induction coil.

magnetic flux set up by the primary links with the secondary, and the above equations do not hold. It is then found easier to determine the secondary induced e.m.f. in terms of the mutual inductance M. Figure 5.14(a) shows the circuit symbol for a *tuned* radio-frequency transformer and Fig. 5.14(b) the constructional details. The primary and secondary are tuned to resonance as discussed in Chapter 6 as this increases the efficiency of the transformer.

Further information on components can be obtained from a companion volume in this series, *Electronic Components, Tubes and Transistors*, by G. W. A. Dummer.

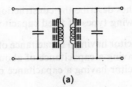

(a)

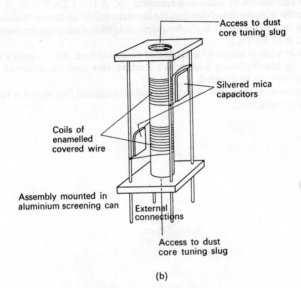

Access to dust core tuning slug

Silvered mica capacitors

Coils of enamelled covered wire

Assembly mounted in aluminium screening can

External connections

Access to dust core tuning slug

(b)

FIG 5.14. A radio-frequency transformer.

5.9. Exercises

1. Sketch and explain the construction of one section of a two-gang variable tuning capacitor for use in a medium-wave broadcast receiver.

What factor determines the shape of the plates of the capacitor? [C & G RLTA, part question].

2. Describe the construction of (a) a preset trimming capacitor as used in a tuned radio circuit, and (b) an electrolytic capacitor.

Quote typical capacitance ranges for both types, and mention two uses of an electrolytic capacitor. [C & G RLTA.]

3. Describe the general form of construction of a wire-wound non-inductive resistor and of a composition type of resistor for use at radio frequencies.

List the advantages and disadvantages of the composition type relative to the wire-wound type. [C & G RLTA.]

4. With the aid of sketches describe the construction, stating the materials used, of TWO of the following types of fixed capacitors:

(a) a silvered mica capacitor having a capacitance of about 500 pF;
(b) a paper capacitor having a capacitance of about 0·5 μF;
(c) an electrolytic capacitor having a capacitance of about 16 μF.

State one application of each, in a receiver.   [C & G RLTA.]

5. Describe with the aid of sketches the construction of an output transformer for use in a high-fidelity audio-frequency amplifier, discussing the material used.   [C & G RLTA.]

6. Explain what is meant by a *laminated* magnetic core. Why is such a core necessary in low-frequency inductors? Explain also how the effect of d.c. magnetization may be avoided.

7. Describe with the aid of sketches the constructional features of a radio-frequency transformer.

CHAPTER 6

SERIES AND PARALLEL TUNED CIRCUITS

6.1. Introduction

The components described in the previous chapter can be connected together in various ways to form electrical circuits. The *tuned* circuit which is essential in radio and line communications will now be described.

6.2. Series tuned circuit (series resonance)

Consider the series circuit of Fig. 6.1 across which a sinusoidal voltage v of frequency f c/s is applied. By making the inductive reactance equal to the capacitive reactance, the voltage across the inductance must be equal to the voltage across the capacitor in magnitude. But the inductive voltage leads the current i by exactly 90°, while the capacitive voltage lags the current by exactly 90°. The various waveforms are shown in Fig. 6.2 and

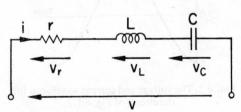

FIG. 6.1. A series tuned circuit.

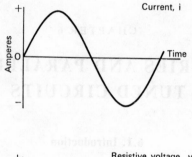

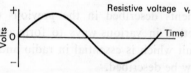

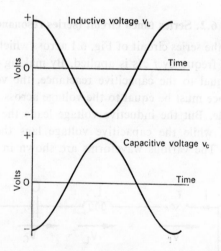

FIG. 6.2. The voltage and current waveforms for
the circuit of Fig. 6.1.

it will be seen that at any instant of time the capacitive voltage exactly cancels the inductive voltage.

This is known as a *resonant* condition, and the adjustment of either C or L to achieve this is known as *tuning*. Both terms originate from the corresponding musical terms.

The frequency at resonance is given by

$$f = \frac{1}{2\pi \sqrt{(LC)}} \quad c/s,$$

where L is in henrys and C is in farads.

At any other frequency the current is less than its resonant value. A curve of the current–frequency is shown in Fig. 6.3(a). A useful guide in obtaining a sketch of the curve is to ask the question: What happens to the current at low frequencies and what happens at very high frequencies? Near zero, capacitive reactance is very high, therefore the opposition to current flow

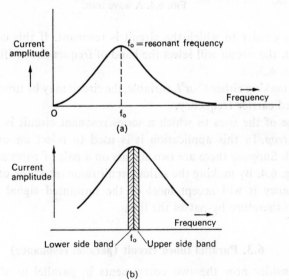

FIG. 6.3. (a) Current–frequency curve for the circuit of Fig. 6.1. (b) Bandwidth selection by means of a tuned circuit.

is high and the current is small. Near infinity, the inductive reactance is very high and, again, the current is small. The current amplitude therefore approaches zero at the extremes of frequency.

The series resonant circuit described is sometimes termed an *acceptor circuit* because it accepts currents at the resonant frequency. If the signal is modulated, as described in Chapter 4, then the side frequencies must not extend too far on either side

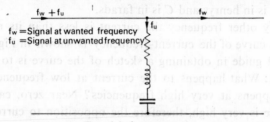

$f_w + f_u$

f_w =Signal at wanted frequency
f_u =Signal at unwanted frequency

f_u

f_w

FIG. 6.4. A wave trap.

of the carrier to which the circuit is resonant. If this condition is met, the circuit will select the band of frequencies as illustrated in Fig. 6.3(b).

By making either C or L variable, the circuit may be tuned to any desired carrier frequency.

One of the uses to which a series resonant circuit is put is a *wave trap*. In this application it is used to reject an unwanted signal. Suppose there are two signals on a pair of wires as shown in Fig. 6.4. By making the series circuit resonant at the unwanted frequency it will accept most of the unwanted signal current, which therefore by-passes the line.

6.3. Parallel tuned circuit (parallel resonance)

Consider now the two components in parallel as shown in Fig. 6.5. The current i_L through the inductive branch lags on the applied voltage by almost 90°, while the current i_C through the capacitor leads the applied voltage by 90°. The total current taken from the supply is

$$i = i_L + i_C,$$

and by tuning the circuit so that i is exactly in phase with v, *the circuit is said to be parallel resonant*. The inductive current i_L will almost cancel the capacitive current i_C, but because of the resistance in the inductive circuit, complete cancellation does not

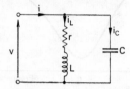

FIG. 6.5. A parallel tuned circuit.

occur at resonance. At resonance, as defined above, neither is the current exactly at its smallest value, but for most practical communications circuits the difference between the true minimum current and the current at resonance is negligible.

The resonant frequency, for all practical purposes is given by

$$f = \frac{1}{2\pi\sqrt{(LC)}} \quad \text{c/s},$$

i.e. the same as for series resonance. The formula is, however, an approximate one for parallel resonance.

The current at resonance will be very small, and at the extremes of frequency can be estimated as follows. At low frequencies the inductive reactance is low, therefore the current will be high, and determined mainly by r (r is often just the inherent series resistance of the coil). At high frequencies the capacitive reactance becomes low, and again the current will be high. The *magnitude* of the current therefore approaches the limits v/r at zero frequency and infinity at infinite frequency. A sketch of the current–frequency curve is shown in Fig. 6.6.

The parallel resonant circuit is sometimes termed a *rejector circuit*, since it rejects currents at the resonant frequency.

One of the chief uses of a parallel circuit is to accept wanted signals while rejecting unwanted signals. Consider again two

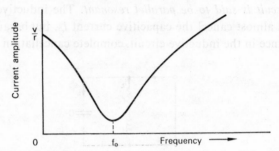

FIG. 6.6. The current–frequency curve for the circuit of Fig. 6.5.

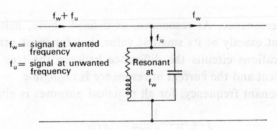

f_w = signal at wanted frequency
f_u = signal at unwanted frequency
Resonant at f_w

FIG. 6.7. Selecting a wanted signal by means of parallel tuning.

signals on a pair of wires, as indicated in Fig. 6.7. By tuning the circuit to the wanted signal frequency the current taken by the circuit at this frequency is very small; therefore most of the signal current continues along the lines. At the unwanted frequency which is not at resonance, the current taken by the circuit is comparatively high, and is therefore by-passed from the line.

Parallel tuned circuits are also widely used in tuned amplifier circuits (see § 10.11).

The phenomenon of resonance is of fundamental importance in all forms of communications systems.

6.4. 3-dB bandwidth

It is important to know how wide a band of frequencies may be selected by a tuned circuit, and to do this some limit must be imposed on the reduction in amplitude which can be tolerated. Theoretically, a signal at any frequency other than the resonant frequency will be reduced in amplitude on passing through the tuned circuit. By convention, it has been agreed to take the frequencies at which the signal power drops to one-half of its resonant value as defining the *bandwidth* of the circuit. Consider the series tuned circuit shown in Fig. 6.8(a). The power taken by the circuit is

$$P = I^2 r.$$

At resonance this can be written as

$$P_0 = I_0^2 r \quad \text{where} \quad I_0 = \text{current at resonance.}$$

If the frequency is altered, two points will be found, one on either side of resonance, at which the power drops to half, and the current at these points can be found as follows:

$$P = \frac{I_0^2 r}{2} = \left(\frac{I_0}{\sqrt{2}}\right)^2 r.$$

Thus, the bandwidth B can be defined by the frequencies at which the current drops to $1/\sqrt{2}$ of its resonant value. This is shown in Fig. 6.8(b). It is easily measured and provides one method of determining the bandwidth of a circuit.

Frequently, the reduction in amplitude is expressed in decibels, and from eqn. (2.1) this is:

$$10 \log_{10} \frac{\frac{1}{2}P}{P} = -10 \log_{10} 2 = -3 \text{ dB.}$$

Alternatively, eqn. (2.5) may be used; thus

$$20 \log_{10} \frac{I_0}{\sqrt{2}\,I} = -20 \log \sqrt{2} = -3 \text{ dB.}$$

Hence the bandwidth defined in this way is known as the 3 dB bandwidth, and is shown in Fig. 6.8(c). A similar result can be shown to hold for the parallel tuned circuit.

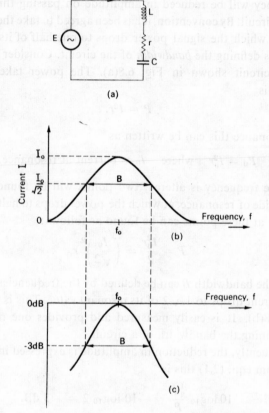

FIG. 6.8. The 3 dB bandwidth of a tuned circuit.

6.5. Worked example

If one section of a two-gang variable tuning capacitor is used to tune the aerial circuit to the incoming signal, calculate the maximum and minimum values of the capacitor required to cover the frequency range 500–1500 c/s when tuned with an inductance of 150 μH. Hence write down the range of the second section required to tune the frequency-changer oscillator over the range 1000–2000 kc/s if the same value of inductance is used to tune the oscillator circuit. [C & G RLTA, part question.]

$$f = \frac{1}{2\pi \sqrt{LC}}.$$

Therefore

$$C = \frac{1}{4\pi^2 f^2 L}.$$

Maximum capacity is required for lowest frequency.

Therefore maximum capacity $= \dfrac{1}{4\pi^2 \times 500^2 \times 10^6 \times 150 \times 10^{-6}}$

$$= \underline{674 \text{ pF}}.$$

$$\text{Minimum capacity} = 674 \times \left(\frac{500}{1500}\right)^2$$

$$= \underline{75 \ \text{pF}}.$$

Oscillator section:

$$\text{Minimum capacity} = 75 \times \left(\frac{1500}{2000}\right)^2$$

$$= \underline{42\cdot 2 \text{ pF}}.$$

$$\text{Maximum capacity} = 75 \times \left(\frac{1500}{1000}\right)^2$$

$$= \underline{169 \text{ pF}}.$$

Hence, the range of capacity for oscillator section

$$= 42\cdot 2\text{–}169 \text{ pF}$$

and the range of capacity for signal section

$$= 75\text{--}674 \text{ pF.}$$

In the above example note the use of proportionality in the calculations; this considerably shortens the work involved. Thus, remember

$$C \alpha \frac{1}{f^2} \quad \text{for a fixed value of } L, \quad \text{and}$$

$$L \alpha \frac{1}{f^2} \quad \text{for a fixed value of } C.$$

6.6. Exercises

1. An inductor having a series resistance of 1 Ω and self-inductance of 500 μH is connected in series with a capacitor of 500 pF. Calculate the frequency at which the circuit impedance appears as a 1 Ω resistance.

2. The inductor of ex. 1 above is connected in parallel with a 200 pF capacitor. Calculate (a) the approximate resonant frequency, and (b) the minimum impedance below resonance. Sketch the curve of impedance against frequency.

3. Explain what is meant by the "3 dB bandwidth" of a tuned circuit. The current at resonance in a series tuned circuit is 2·5 mA, and this is found to drop by 3 dB at frequencies of 210 kc/s and 220 kc/s. Calculate (a) the bandwidth of the circuit, and (b) the circuit current at each bandwidth limit.

CHAPTER 7

ELECTRO-ACOUSTIC
DEVICES

7.1. Introduction

Much of the art of telecommunications is concerned with the transmission of sound by electrical means. At the sending end, the sound is converted into an electrical signal by means of a *microphone* (often referred to as a *transmitter* in telephone engineering). At the receiving end, the electrical signal is converted back to sound by means of a telephone *receiver*, in the normal telephone, or by means of a *loud-speaker*, where a larger volume of sound is required.

A variety of microphone types are in use. These range from the simple and cheap carbon microphone which only costs a few shillings, to the costly capacitor microphone. Loud-speakers, too, range widely in cost, depending on the quality and performance required, and the type of enclosure provided with the speaker. In this chapter, only a few of the types will be examined.

7.2. Microphones

The carbon microphone

The electrical circuit of this type of microphone is simply a resistance which can be varied by means of sound waves (Fig. 7.1). The resistance is connected in series with a d.c. supply and load

R_L. Sound waves reaching the microphone produce variations in the microphone resistance r, which in turn modulate the current.

The circuit current is inversely proportional to resistance. Therefore, if variations in resistance are proportional to the sound-wave variations, the resulting current will be distorted. This distortion is shown in the following example.

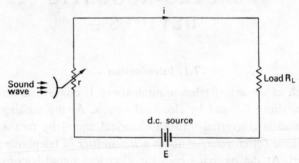

FIG. 7.1. The carbon microphone as a resistor.

Let
$$E = 6 \text{ V},$$
$$r_0 + R_L = 100 \ \Omega,$$

and, initially, assume that the sound wave is sinusoidal and produces a sinusoidal variation in r of $\pm 50 \ \Omega$ peak. This is shown in Fig. 7.2(a).

The direct current will be

$$I_{dc} = \frac{6}{100} \text{ A} \quad \text{or} \quad 60 \text{ mA}.$$

The current maximum will be

$$I_{max} = \frac{6}{100 - 50} \text{ A} \quad \text{or} \quad 120 \text{ mA}.$$

The current minimum will be

$$I_{min} = \frac{6}{100 - 50} \text{ A} \quad \text{or} \quad 40 \text{ mA}.$$

Thus the variation in current will have peak values of $+60$ mA and -20 mA about the d.c. value. This is shown in Fig. 7.2(b), where it can be seen that the variation is not sinusoidal.

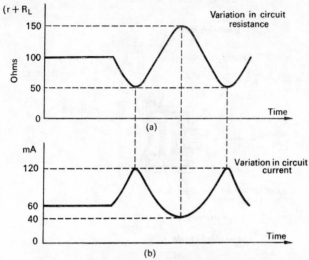

FIG. 7.2. (a) Sinusoidal variation of microphone resistance with time. (b) The corresponding non-sinusoidal current wave.

This inherent distortion with the carbon michrophone can only be reduced by keeping the variation in r small compared with the total circuit resistance. If in the previous example the variation in resistance is limited to a sinusoidal variation of $\pm 5\,\Omega$, then:

$$I_{dc} = \frac{6}{100}\ \text{A} \quad \text{or} \quad 60\ \text{mA as before,}$$

$$I_{max} = \frac{6}{100-5}\ \text{A} \quad \text{or} \quad 63\cdot2\ \text{mA,}$$

$$I_{min} = \frac{6}{100+5}\ \text{A} \quad \text{or} \quad 57\cdot2\ \text{mA.}$$

It will be seen that the current is more nearly sinusoidal. It will also be observed that the reduction in distortion is only obtained at the expense of a reduction in output.

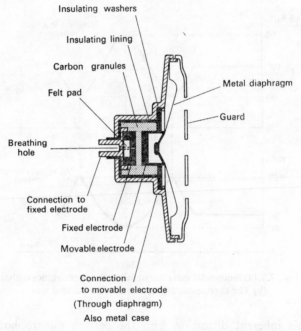

FIG. 7.3. A single-button carbon microphone.

The essential constructional features of a modern carbon microphone are shown in Fig. 7.3. The microphone resistance consists mainly of carbon granules packed between two carbon electrodes—one fixed, one movable. The movable electrode is attached to a thin metal diaphragm which is vibrated by the sound wave. In this way the sound vibrations are transferred to pressure variations on the carbon granules. The granules may be considered as very small spheres in contact and forming an electrical path from one electrode to the other. When the pressure increases, these spheres are slightly flattened, and therefore the contact area is increased. The electrical resistance is therefore decreased. When the pressure decreases, fewer of the granules make contact with others and the electrical resistance increases. The connection to the movable electrode is through the metal case and the metal diaphragm. The connection to the fixed electrode is through a metal socket at the back. A small hole is provided through this socket which allows the air pressure within the carbon granule chamber to equalize to the average outside pressure. This is termed a breathing hole.

The carbon microphone described is widely used in telephones throughout the world, its main advantages for this application being (a) it is inexpensive, (b) it is robust, (c) it has high sensitivity, (d) it gives fairly good quality speech reproduction.

In connection with (c) it should be noted that the carbon microphone can act as a power amplifier. A given variation of input sound power can result in a much greater variation of electrical power from the d.c. source.

The main disadvantages of the carbon microphone are (a) it generates a considerable amount of noise, known as *flicker noise*, and which appears in the output as a background hiss, and (b) its frequency response is uneven and the output falls off rapidly at high frequencies. Thus it is not suitable for high quality sound reproduction. The frequency response is considered in more detail in § 7.3.

The impedance of the carbon microphone ranges from about $10\,\Omega$ to $100\,\Omega$ resistive. When used to feed a voltage amplifier, a step-up transformer of about $1:50$ is employed, and when used in power circuits, as, for example, feeding a telephone line, a step-up transformer of about $1:3$ is employed.

The moving-coil microphone

This is a *generator* type microphone. The diaphragm is attached to a coil situated in a powerful permanent magnet field. Movement of the diaphragm results in an e.m.f. being induced in the coil. Figure 7.4 shows the essential constructional features of a modern moving-coil microphone. The magnet may be cylindrically shaped or it may be in the form of a "truncated cone" as shown. The cylindrical casing forms part of the magnetic circuit, the bottom of the case being joined to the magnet through the back plate. A pole piece, attached to the top of the magnet, completes the

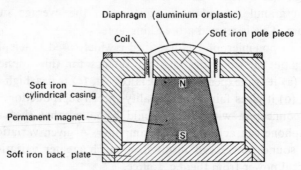

Diaphragm (aluminium or plastic)

Coil

Soft iron pole piece

Soft iron cylindrical casing

N

Permanent magnet

S

Soft iron back plate

FIG. 7.4. A moving-coil microphone.

magnetic circuit through the iron. The coil moves in the air gap between the pole piece and the top of the case.

The output of the moving-coil microphone is considerably less than that of the carbon microphone for a given input. However, it is capable of providing a much better frequency response (see § 7.3) and, in general, it is a more versatile type of microphone. Models available range from cheap general purpose microphones to expensive studio microphones.

Moving-coil microphones made in Britain and the U.S.A. usually have impedances in the range 20–30 Ω while European manufacturers have standardized on the higher value of 200 Ω. The higher impedance type generates a higher e.m.f. but requires a coil of much finer wire compared with the low impedance type, and is therefore less robust.

The crystal microphone

Certain materials, such as quartz crystal, Rochelle salt crystal, and some ceramics, develop an e.m.f. when subjected to mechanical stress and also show the opposite effect of mechanically

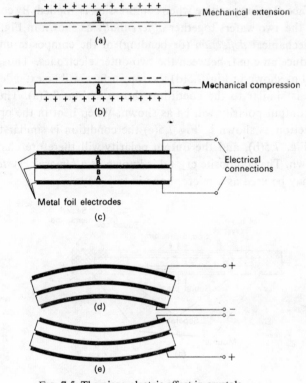

FIG. 7.5. The piezo-electric effect in crystals.

contracting and extending when an e.m.f. of appropriate polarity is applied. This effect is known as the *piezoelectric effect*, and it finds a variety of applications in telecommunications. One obvious use is as a microphone, and for this the Rochelle salt crystal is found to be the most suitable.

Figure 7.5 illustrates how a basic microphone unit is constructed. Two very thin wafers of Rochelle salt crystals are used. Figure 7.5(a) shows the surface A going positive and surface B going negative when a mechanical extension is applied to the wafer as shown. Figure 7.5(b) shows surface A going negative and surface B going positive when compression is applied. By connecting the two wafers together *differentially* as shown in Fig. 7.5(c) a mechanical *deflection* (or bending) of the composite unit will produce an e.m.f. between the two outer electrodes. Thus, when bent as shown in Fig. 7.5(d) the top surface will be extended, and this is similar to the condition shown in Fig. 7.5(a). Therefore the output polarity will be as shown. When bent in the opposite direction as shown in Fig 7.5(e) the condition is similar to that in Fig. 7.5(b), and the output polarity will therefore change as shown. The composite crystal is known as a *bimorph crystal*, and it may be used as a microphone in two ways.

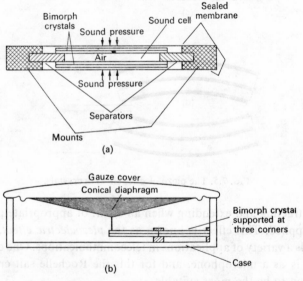

FIG. 7.6. The piezo-electric or crystal microphone.

Figure 7.6(a) illustrates the construction of a high quality microphone utilizing the bimorph crystal. In this, two bimorph crystals are assembled together to form a *sound cell*, and the sound wave acts directly on the exposed surfaces of the cell. A number of sound cells may be used in one microphone and connected in series—parallel to increase the output. Each cell is very small, being about 1·5 mm square by 0·12 mm thick. Because of the small physical size of the cells, mechanical resonances occur well outside the audio-frequency range, and the microphone has a flat frequency response (see § 7.3). The output voltage depends on the number of cells used, and is of the same order as the moving-coil microphone. The output impedance is very high, and is formed essentially by the small capacity between the foil electrodes.

A more robust and more sensitive type of crystal microphone is illustrated in Fig. 7.6(b). Here a mechanical diaphragm is used to transfer the sound waves to a bimorph crystal, and by using a large diaphragm the electrical output may be increased. The disadvantage of this type is that the diaphragm system introduces mechanical resonances which affect the frequency response of the microphone within the audio-frequency range. However, the diaphragm type finds wide, general-purpose use.

Crystal microphones are not suitable for use at temperatures above about 100°F, as the piezoelectric effect of Rochelle salt decreases very rapidly above this temperature.

7.3. Frequency response of microphones

The frequency response curve of a microphone shows how the electrical output varies as the frequency of the sound input is varied, all other factors (such as amplitude of input) remaining constant. The moving parts of any microphone will have a mechanical resonance frequency determined by the *mass* of the moving system and the *stiffness* of the movement. The output at the reso-

nant frequency will be higher than at other frequencies, and will
be limited by the *mechanical resistance* to motion. A sharp output
peak at one particular frequency is undesirable, and therefore it
is necessary to reduce the effect of mechanical resonance. This
could be damped out by adding mechanical resistance, but such

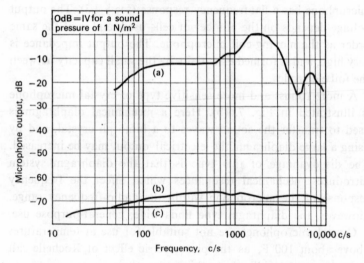

FIG. 7.7. The frequency response curves for the microphones described.

a method is wasteful of energy; usually, the resonance is only partly
damped, and *acoustic cavities* are built into the microphone
which produce additional resonances. These tend to smooth out
the response curve at a higher level than that which would have
been achieved with damping alone.

The frequency response curves for the microphones described
are shown in Fig. 7.7.

7.4. Polar response of microphones

A microphone may have directional characteristics. For example, some microphones will only produce an output when the sound wave approaches from the front. Other types produce an output no matter from which direction the sound comes. The way in which output varies with direction is usually shown graphically in a form known as a *polar diagram*. The pole of the graph represents the position of the microphone, and the zero angle line is *normal*, i.e. at right angles to the front of the microphone. It is assumed that the microphone is mounted level, and direction is measured in the horizontal plane cutting the centre of the microphone.

The polar response of a microphone depends to a large extent on the frequency of the sound wave. Over most of the speech band 300–3400 c/s, the types of microphones described have *omnidirectional* responses, i.e. they respond equally well to sound from all directions. However, at high audio-frequencies, where the wavelength is comparable with the dimensions of the microphone, considerable attenuation occurs for sound approaching from the sides and the rear of the microphone. The polar diagram is then modified from the omnidirectional response shown as curve (i), Fig. 7.8(a), to curve (ii). The curves shown in Fig. 7.8(b) result when the microphone is *pressure operated*. This means that it is only the front of the microphone that is open to the sound wave, and the diaphragm is actuated by the sound pressure.

Where it is possible to provide a controlled air path through the microphone, part of the diaphragm is actuated by the *pressure difference* between the back and front of the diaphragm. The velocity at which the diaphragm moves is proportional to the pressure difference, and because of this, the term *velocity microphone* is sometimes used. With this mode of operation it is possible to obtain a *cardioid* (i.e. heart-shaped) polar diagram. This type of microphone is very useful as it discriminates against unwanted noise from the rear. Of the microphones described, only the moving-coil type can be arranged in practice to have a cardioid polar response.

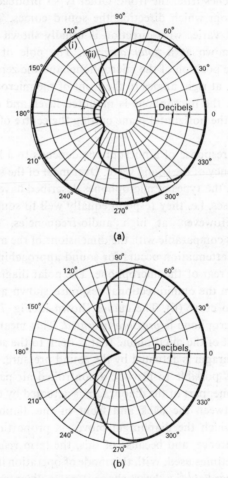

(a)

(b)

FIG. 7.8. (a) Polar response curves at low and high frequencies. (b) A cardioid polar response.

7.5. Telephone receivers

Fig. 7.9(a) shows the essential features of the type of receiver most commonly encountered in telephones, and Fig. 7.9(b) the magnetic circuit. A powerful permanent magnet exerts a constant pull on a thin magnetic diaphragm. The electrical signal (representing the sound wave) passes through coils wound around the pole pieces of the magnet, and the magnetic field set up by this electromagnetic system will alternate about the steady field produced by the magnet. The diaphragm will vibrate in sympathy with the alternating component of pull, and in this way it generates a sound wave related to the electrical signal. The coils must be wound in opposite directions on the pole pieces, as shown in Fig. 7.9(b), in order to produce the correct magnetic polarity at all times.

The permanent magnet is an essential feature of this type of receiver. To understand this it must be appreciated that the pull on the diaphragm is proportional to the total flux-density *squared*. Without the permanent magnet, a negative-going signal produces a negative-going flux density (i.e. a reversal of direction), but because of the square law the reversal is not apparent in the output. With the permanent magnet present, a negative-going signal reduces the total flux density, but this remains positive provided the permanent flux density is greater than the peak signal value, a condition which must be met in practice. Thus a negative-going signal is apparent as a reduction in the pull on the diaphragm, and a positive-going signal as an increase in the pull, about the steady pull exerted by the permanent magnet.

Also because of the square law the larger the permanent flux density the greater will be the output.

In order to achieve a high flux density, high permeability materials are used in the magnetic circuit, these materials being indicated in Fig. 7.9(a). The diaphragm also has a high resistivity to reduce losses resulting from eddy currents.

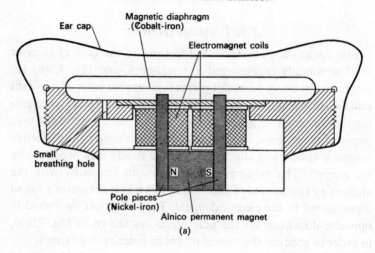

(a)

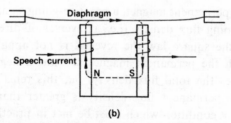

(b)

FIG. 7.9. (a) A magnetic diaphragm receiver. (b) The magnetic circuit for (a).

The rocking-armature receiver

The principle of operation of this type is illustrated in Fig. 7.10. The permanent magnetic flux divides equally through the armature which under no-signal conditions is held in balance. When a signal current flows through the coils, the magnetic field through one limb is strengthened while that through the other limb is weakened. The result is that the armature rocks about its pivot, depending on the polarity of the signal current.

This type of receiver has a higher output than the type previously described due to the fact that the permanent magnetic flux has two paths in parallel with a consequent increase in the total flux.

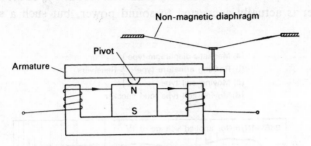

Fig. 7.10. A rocking-armature receiver.

The moving-coil receiver

The construction of this is similar to the moving-coil microphone already described (see Fig. 7.4) and with proper design one unit may be used either as microphone or receiver. Used as a receiver, the signal current is passed through the moving coil, and the magnetic field set up alternately aids and opposes the permanent magnet field. Thus the forces of attraction and repulsion on the coil vibrate the diaphragm in sympathy with the signal. The moving-coil receiver is used mainly in high quality headphones.

7.6. Frequency response and power of telephone receivers

The diaphragm of a receiver must move the air mass surrounding it. As with a microphone, there will be some frequencies at which the diaphragm is more efficient, due to mechanical resonances. Figure 7.11 shows the frequency response curves for the three types of receivers described. It will be seen that the response curves are similar and adequately cover the range 300–3400 c/s required for speech.

The input power to a telephone receiver is of the order 0·1 mW, needed to produce a satisfactory loudness. About 1 % of the input power is actually converted to sound power, but such a small

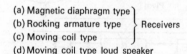

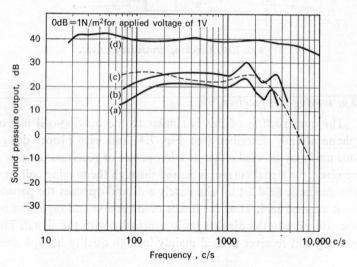

Fig. 7.11. Frequency response curves for receivers.

power is adequate because the receiver is always operated close to the ear. Also because of this, the polar diagram of the receiver is not important.

Typical impedance values are 300 Ω for the magnetic diaphragm and rocking-armature types, and 20 Ω for the moving-coil type.

7.7. The moving-coil loud-speaker

The main constructional features are shown in Fig. 7.12(a), and Fig. 7.12(b) shows a sketch of a typical speaker. A light coil is attached to a cone (which takes the place of a diaphragm),

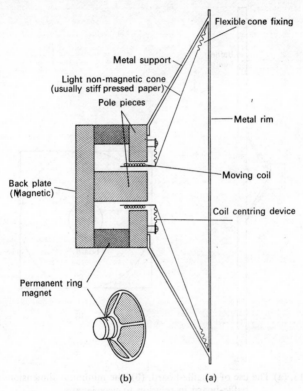

FIG. 7.12. A moving-coil loud-speaker.

and is free to move to and fro in a strong constant magnetic field. The signal current is passed through the coil, and the resulting magnetic field is either attracted by or repelled by the permanent field. As the signal alternates in polarity, the direction of movement of the coil alternates, causing the cone to vibrate.

It will be seen that the action is similar to that of the moving-coil receiver. The coil is often referred to as the *speech coil*. The speech coil must be prevented from fouling the pole pieces, and it is held in the centre of the air gap by means of a flexible ring.

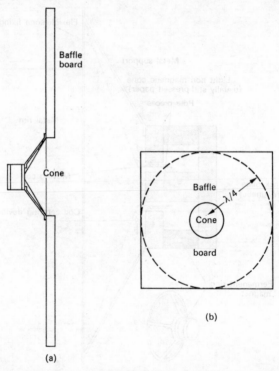

FIG. 7.13. (a) The use of a baffle-board. (b) The minimum dimensions for a baffle-board in relation to wavelength.

This allows to-and-fro movement while preventing sideways movement.

At low frequencies the cone moves rather like a piston, and at high frequencies the movement is much more complex, it being possible for different sections of the cone to vibrate independently of each other.

A *baffle-board* is necessary to prevent the sound wave from the front of the cone cancelling that from the back, since a decrease in air pressure is created at the back simultaneously with an increase at the front, and vice versa. The baffle-board isolates the front of the speaker from the back, as shown in Fig. 7.13(a). The larger the baffle-board the better will be the isolation, but there is obviously a practical limit to its size. In practice, the baffle size is determined by the lowest frequency which must be reproduced without loss of power, and it is found that the baffle must extend at least one-quarter of a wavelength at this frequency around the speaker, as shown in Fig. 7.13(b). The baffle must be made of stout material, e.g. $\frac{3}{4}$ in. plywood in order to prevent it resonating.

7.8. Frequency response and power of the moving-coil speaker

A loud-speaker may be required to reproduce frequencies ranging from about 30 c/s to 10,000 c/s without showing undue peaks or resonances. In order to produce sufficient baffle effect, the loud-speaker is usually mounted inside a cabinet. The cabinet must be constructed of heavy material in order to prevent the sides resonating and in some cases brick enclosures have been used. For good results the inside of the cabinet (or enclosure) should be lined with sound-absorbent material to prevent reflections occurring within the cabinet. A small hole, or port, is sometimes provided, and this couples sound energy from the back to the front of the speaker, but with the correct phase relationship for it to be additive.

Moving-coil loud-speakers are about 5% efficient, that is, they convert about 5% of the electrical energy into sound energy. The input power to the speaker depends on the application of the speaker. In a radio receiver, 50 mW may be taken as average, while in a high-fidelity reproducing system intended for use in a large room, power inputs of the order 10–20 W may be encountered.

Common values of impedance for the moving-coil loud-speaker are: 3 Ω where the speaker is mounted close to the signal source, and 15 Ω where long connecting leads must be used between speaker and source.

7.9. Exercises

1. Explain, by reference to the operation of a simple two-way telephone circuit, the function of :

(a) the permanent magnet in the telephone receiver,
(b) the direct current in the carbon microphone.   [C & G RLT A, 1961.]

2. Describe with the aid of sketches the construction and operation of:

(a) a moving-coil telephone receiver,
(b) a moving-iron telephone receiver.

Briefly explain the effect on the operation of each type if the permanent magnet is removed.   [C & G RLT A, 1963–4.]

3. Describe with the aid of a sketch the constructional features and principle of operation of the carbon-granule microphone.

Explain clearly, using a diagram, how the output alternating energy is derived.   [C & G RLT A, 1960.]

4. A carbon-granule microphone has an unmodulated resistance of 50 Ω and is connected in a telephone circuit of series resistance 50 Ω, and d.c. supply voltage of 12 V. Calculate the direct current and the positive and negative variations about the d.c. value when a sinusoidal sound wave results in a $\pm 10\%$ variation in microphone resistance.

5. The output of a microphone, in decibels relative to 1 V/N/m², for various frequencies, is given in the following table. Plot the frequency response characteristic.

If the output voltage is 10 mV at 1000 c/s for a given sound pressure, what is the output voltage at 3000 c/s for the same pressure? (It may be assumed that the curve is smooth over the range of frequencies given.)

Frequency (kc/s)	0·05	0·06	0·08	0·1	0·2	0·5	1·0	2·0	4·0	5·0
Output (dB)	1·0	0·5	0·0	0·5	1·5	2·0	1·5	1·0	−1·0	−3·0

6. The polar response characteristics of a microphone are as shown in the table below, where the decibel reference is maximum (arbitrary) output voltage. Assuming that the polar response is symmetrical about the 0–180° line, draw the polar curve.

Direction	0°	30°	60°	80°	90°	100°	120°	150°	180°
Output (dB)	0	0	0	−2	−4	−5	−8	−11	−15

CHAPTER 8

SEMICONDUCTOR AND THERMIONIC DEVICES

8.1. Introduction

In Chapter 5 the nature of resistivity and conductivity is discussed, and Fig. 8.1 illustrates further the range of values obtainable for different materials. Of special interest here are the semiconductor materials silicon and germanium. The atoms in these two materials have a similar regular arrangement, known as a *cubic lattice*. Each atom has four outermost, or *valence* electrons, and these form the bonds with neighbouring atoms, known as the *covalent bonds*.

8.2. *n* and *p* materials

By diffusing into germanium or silicon a material which has five valence electrons to each atom, one electron becomes free, since only four are required to form the covalent bonds. The free electron is readily removed from the vicinity of its parent atom, and becomes available as a negative carrier of electricity. Germanium or silicon which has been treated in this way is known as *n-type* material because the current carriers are electrons which are negatively charged. The added material is termed an *impurity*, and in this case, since it gives an electron for conduction, it is known as a *donor impurity*. The process of adding the impurity is referred to as *doping*. Typical donor impurities are arsenic, phosphorus and antimony.

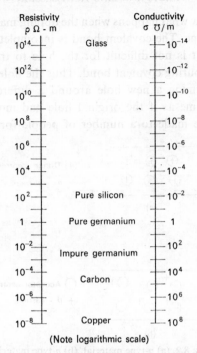

(Note logarithmic scale)

FIG. 8.1. Resistivity and conductivity of various materials.

When a donor atom forms part of the crystal structure in germanium or silicon, it loses one electron and thus becomes positively charged. This charge is rigidly fixed in position within the material and is known as a *donor centre*. It will be seen, therefore, that the net electric charge in the doped material is still zero although the negative charges are free to move and the positive charges are fixed in position. Figure 8.2(a) illustrates, in symbolic form, *n*-type material, the properties of which may be summarized as:

n-type material

    Mobile negative charges or *n*-carriers.

    Fixed positive charges (donor centres).

Consider now what happens when the doping material has three valence electrons. The covalent bond is incomplete and a *hole* is said to exist. It is not difficult for the hole to trap an electron from a neighbouring covalent bond. Thus the hole is filled at the expense of forming a new hole around a different atom. The effect is the same as if the original hole had moved. A simple analogy can be made to a number of people forming a queue.

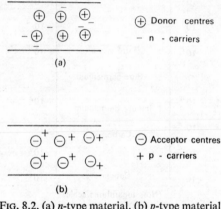

(a)

(b)

FIG. 8.2. (a) *n*-type material. (b) *p*-type material.

If the person at the head of the queue moves away the others shuffle forward one place and the vacant space soon appears at the tail of the queue.

Holes "moving" in one direction are equivalent to electrons moving in the opposite direction; thus the movement of electric charge may be considered as negative charge moving in the direction of the electrons or positive charge moving in the direction of the holes. In such a situation it is easier to deal with hole movement. The holes are *positive carriers*, and the material is known as *p-type*.

The impurity added in this case is termed an *acceptor impurity* since it accepts an electron from a neighbouring atom. Acceptor centres are rigidly fixed in the material, and when they gain an extra electron they have a net negative charge. The properties of *p*-type material are:

p-type material
    Mobile positive charges or *p*-carriers.
    Fixed negative charges (acceptor centres).

p-type material is illustrated in Fig. 8.2(b). As with *n*-type, the overall charge is zero. Typical acceptor impurities are gallium, indium, boron and aluminium.

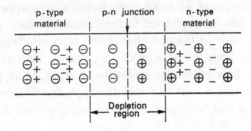

FIG. 8.3. The *p–n* junction.

An important behaviour, characteristic of carriers, is that of *diffusion*, i.e. carriers tend to spread or diffuse throughout the material. If, therefore, a piece of material is doped *p*-type in one-half and *n*-type in the other, diffusion of positive and negative carriers will occur simultaneously throughout the material. Immediately the carriers diffuse across the *p–n* junction, a potential difference is set up between donor and acceptor centres. The polarity of this is such as to retard further diffusion. The diffusion process in effect generates a *potential barrier*, and eventually an equilibrium state must be reached. The junction is termed a *p–n junction*, and the region around the junction from which carriers have diffused is known as the *depletion region*. The *p–n* junction plays an important part in all semiconductor devices, and the various sections associated with it are shown in Fig. 8.3.

During the process of diffusion some electrons must collide with holes, in which case the electron fills the hole. This is termed *recombination*, and it assists in creating the potential barrier. However, the predominant factor is the diffusion process.

8.3. The *p–n* junction

It was seen that a material suitably doped with donor and acceptor impurities generated an internal potential barrier which stopped movement of holes and electrons across the junction. A battery may be connected to the junction in such a way that its voltage adds to the potential of the junction. This is termed *reverse bias*, since the polarity of the battery is such as to further oppose the flow of current across the junction. In an ideal junction, no current would flow with the application of reverse bias. However, it will be shown in the following section that a small current does flow in practical junctions.

By reversing the battery connections the battery voltage is made to oppose the junction potential. This is termed *forward bias*, since the battery reduces the effectiveness of the potential barrier and causes current to flow.

An easy way of remembering the connections for a required bias is to imagine that the positive terminal of the battery repels the positive carriers (i.e. holes) in the *p*-material across the junction; thus current flows. Therefore the positive terminal of the battery is connected to the *p*-material for forward bias. The reverse is true for the reverse bias. The methods of connection are shown in Fig. 8.4.

The curves of current against battery voltage are also shown in Fig. 8.4. The forward current rises rapidly with increase in forward bias once this exceeds the junction potential. The curve of I_F against V_F is not exactly a straight line, but for many purposes can be assumed to be linear.

The current with reverse bias is due to what is known as

minority carriers in the material. Heat and light energy are capable of disrupting covalent bonds, and wherever this occurs in the material, a hole-electron pair is formed. These are generated at random throughout the material, and therefore some holes will appear in the *n*-material, and some electrons in the *p*-material. The field due to the reverse bias, plus that due to the

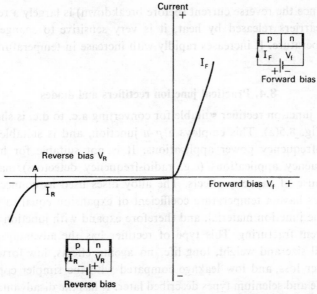

FIG. 8.4. Forward and reverse characteristics of a *p–n* junction.

function, will move holes from *n* to *p*, and electrons from *p* to *n*. This movement of minority carriers constitutes the reverse current.

The availability of minority carriers depends to a large extent on the external heat or light energy absorbed by the *p–n* materials, and is almost independent of reverse bias. The current is a saturation current since with a small applied voltage all the available carriers are used. When the applied voltage is large enough, however, it imparts sufficient energy to the minority carriers for them to disrupt additional covalent bonds through collision. The effect is cumulative, and is known as the *avalanche effect*. The voltage at which this occurs is shown as A on Fig. 8.4. Beyond this reverse voltage, the reverse current increases very rapidly indeed, and if allowed to continue will cause breakdown of the junction.

Since the reverse current (before breakdown) is largely a result of carriers released by heat, it is very sensitive to changes in temperature. It increases rapidly with increase in temperature.

8.4. Practical junction rectifiers and diodes

A junction rectifier suitable for converting a.c. to d.c. is shown in Fig. 8.5(a). This employs a *p–n* junction, and is suitable for low-frequency power applications. It is not suitable for high-frequency applications (e.g. radio-frequency detectors) mainly because of capacity effects. The alloy discs used as connecting plates have a temperature coefficient of expansion equal to that of the junction material, and therefore expand with junction and prevent fracturing. This type of rectifier has the advantages of small size and weight, long life, no ageing effects, low forward power loss, and low leakage compared with the simpler copper oxide and selenium types described later. It has the disadvantages of being adversely affected by high temperatures and humidity.

It is found that when a *p*- or *n*-type material is in contact with a conducting surface, diffusion occurs, forming a potential barrier in the manner described previously. Diffusion is greater for some conducting surfaces than others, and it is possible to arrange for a potential barrier to occur at one contact and not at the other, by suitable selection of material. This is the basis of the copper oxide rectifier and the selenium rectifier, illustrated in Figs. 8.5(b) and (c) respectively. Copper oxide occurs naturally as a *p*-type material and forms a potential barrier at the copper contact but not at the graphite and lead contact. Forward bias is achieved by connecting the positive terminal of the battery to the lead contact and the negative terminal to the copper contact.

Selenium also occurs naturally as a *p*-type material and can be used as a rectifier. The barrier is formed at the tin-alloy contact, and not at the nickel–steel contact. Forward bias is achieved by connecting the positive terminal of the battery to the steel contact and the negative terminal to the tin alloy. The selenium

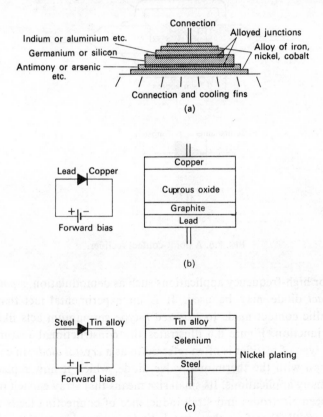

FIG. 8.5. (a) A *p–n* junction suitable for power rectification. (b) The elements of a copper-oxide rectifier. (c) The elements of a selenium rectifier.

rectifier has a number of advantages over the copper-oxide type. Chiefly, it can handle higher reverse voltages before breaking down; it is less affected by temperature; and it is easier to make good electrical contact to the rectifying element.

Often the elements are stacked in series on a rod, spacing washers being inserted between elements to allow for cooling.

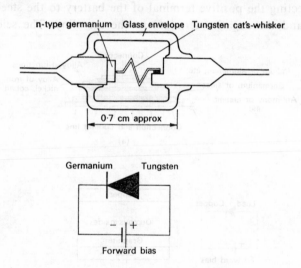

FIG. 8.6. A point-contact rectifier.

For high-frequency applications such as demodulation, a *point-contact* diode may be used. It is an experimental fact that a metallic contact made to oxidized *n*-type germanium acts like a *p–n* junction. Figure 8.6 illustrates the constructional features. This type of rectifier is often referred to as a *crystal diode*, in comparison with the thermionic valve diode, which it now replaces for many applications. Its small size means that stray capacitance between electrodes and stray inductance of connecting leads are very small, therefore the crystal diode is superior to the valve diode at very high frequencies.

8.5. The junction transistor

The junction transistor consists essentially of two *p–n* junction arranged as shown in Fig 8.7(a) or (b). Both arrangements are used in practice. The three sections of the transistor are known as the *emitter*, the *base* and the *collector*. The emitter *emits* current carriers and corresponds to the cathode in a thermionic

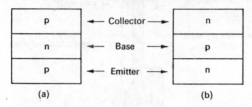

FIG. 8.7. (a) A *p-n-p* transistor. (b) A *n-p-n* transistor.

valve. The collector *collects* the current carriers, and corresponds to the anode in a valve. The base provides the control link between emitter and collector, and in this respect corresponds to the control grid in a triode valve.

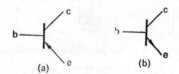

FIG. 8.8. Circuit symbols for the transistor.

The graphic symbol for a transistor is shown in Fig. 8.8. Figure 8.8(a) is the symbol for the *p–n–p* type, and Fig. 8.8(b) for the *n–p–n* type. The only difference between the symbols is the direction of the arrow representing the emitter. In both cases this points in the direction of conventional current or hole flow.

The word transistor describes a fundamental property of the device, relating input and output resistance, and is coined from the words *trans*fer res*istor*.

A silicon transistor (OC200) of the alloy type is illustrated in Fig. 8.9.

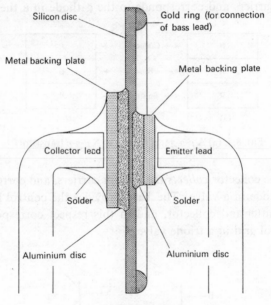

FIG. 8.9. A silicon alloy-type transistor.
(Courtesy Mullard Ltd.)

In the operation of the transistor, the collector–base junction is reverse biased, and the emitter–base junction is forward biased. This is achieved for a *p–n–p* transistor as shown in Fig. 8.10. The forward bias on the emitter–base junction enables this to conduct easily, so that the collector–base battery may be connected to the emitter rather than to the base while still biasing the collector–base junction in reverse.

The forward bias applied to the base–emitter junction permits carriers to move from emitter into the base. These, in the base, are minority carriers (e.g. *p*-type carriers in the *n*-type base shown in Fig. 8.10), and are therefore swept into the collector circuit by the reverse bias across the collector–base junction. Thus the collector current can be controlled by the current in the base–emitter circuit.

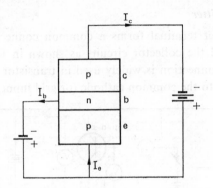

FIG. 8.10. Bias arrangement for a transistor.

It will be seen that for the direct-current conditions shown in Fig. 8.10 the emitter current (I_e), must equal the sum of the base and collector currents. For example, if I_e is 1·0 mA and I_c is 0·98 mA, the base current would be 20 μA. By convention, currents flowing into the transistor are considered positive and those flowing out negative (although this in not always shown on manufacturers' data).

The relationships between voltages and currents are usually presented in graphical form, known as the *static characteristic curves*, and these will be examined before the amplifying action of the transistor is considered.

8.6. Static characteristic curves of a transistor

A transistor may be connected in one of three modes known as *common emitter*, *common base* and *common collector*, and the static characteristic curves in general depend on the mode of connection. Only the first two modes will be examined in this volume.

Common emitter

The emitter terminal forms a common connection for both the base and the collector circuits as shown in Fig. 8.11. This method of connection is widely used in transistor circuitry, and corresponds to the common cathode (or grid input) valve circuit.

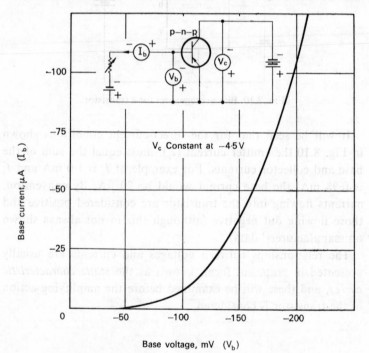

V_c Constant at −4·5 V

Base current, μA (I_b)

Base voltage, mV (V_b)

FIG. 8.11. The input characteristic for common emitter.

Common base

The base terminal forms a common connection for emitter and collector circuits, as shown in Fig. 8.12. This corresponds to the earthed grid—or grounded grid—method of connection

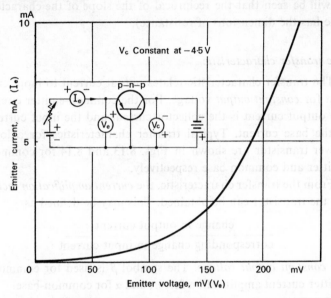

FIG. 8.12. The input characteristic for common base.

for valves. The common-base circuit is not as widely used as the common-emitter circuit, but it has some advantages which suit it for particular applications.

Some of the differences will be apparent after examination of the static characteristic curves.

The input characteristic

This is a curve which relates the input current to the input voltage for *constant collector voltage*. A typical input characteristic for a common-emitter connection is shown in Fig. 8.11, and for a common-base connection in Fig. 8.12. These are typical for low-power transistors, e.g. capable of handling milliwatts of power. The input characteristic gives a rough guide to the value of *input resistance* for the particular type of connection used (it will be seen that the reciprocal of the slope of the characteristic has the dimensions of resistance).

The transfer characteristic

The transfer characteristic relates output current to input current for *constant output* voltage. For the common-emitter circuit the output current is the collector current and the input current is the base current. Typical transfer characteristics for a low-power transistor are shown in Figs. 8.13 and 8.14 for common emitter and common base respectively.

From the transfer characteristic, the *current amplification factor* for the transistor can be obtained. This may be defined as

$$\frac{\text{change in output current}}{\text{corresponding change in input current}}$$

for *constant output voltage*. The symbol β is used for common-emitter current amplification factor, and α for common-base.

From Fig. 8.13 $\beta = \dfrac{4900}{100} = 49$.

From Fig. 8.14 $\alpha = \dfrac{9 \cdot 8}{10} = 0 \cdot 98$.

These values are typical for low-power transistors used in common-emitter and common-base modes, respectively.

It will be shown in volume 2 that,

$$\beta = \frac{\alpha}{1-\alpha},$$

e.g. $49 = \dfrac{0 \cdot 98}{0 \cdot 62}$ for the above figures.

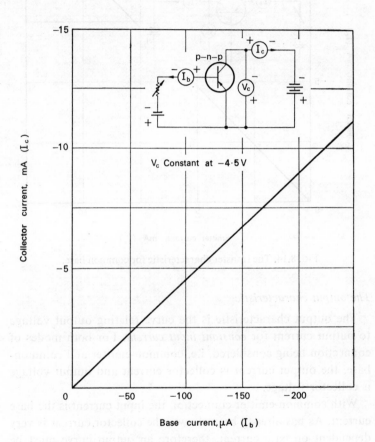

FIG. 8.13. The transfer characteristic for common emitter.

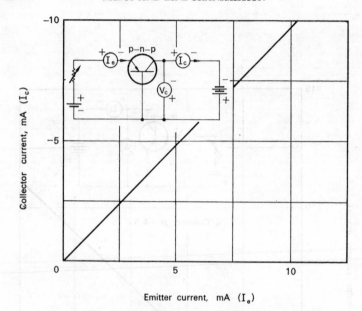

Fig. 8.14. The transfer characteristic for common base.

The output characteristic

The output characteristic is the curve relating output voltage to output current for *constant input current*. For both modes of connection being considered, i.e. common-emitter and common-base, the output current is collector current and output voltage is collector voltage.

With common-emitter connection the input current is the base current. As has already been shown, the collector current is very dependent on base current, therefore an output curve must be obtained for each of several values of base current. The resulting set of curves is known as a *family of output characteristic curves*.

A typical family of curves for the common-emitter circuit is shown in Fig. 8.15 along with a circuit which may be used to obtain these. It should be noted that in measuring voltages in transistor circuits, high-impedance voltmeters should be used. The output curves give a rough guide to the value of *output resistance* for the particular mode of connection used (again, it will be seen that the reciprocal of the slope of the characteristic has the dimensions of resistance).

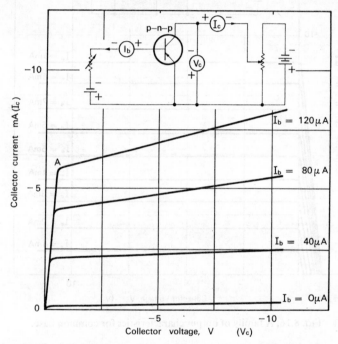

FIG. 8.15. A family of output characteristics for common emitter.

Beyond the line *OA* (Fig. 8.15), a large change in collector voltage produces only a small change in collector current. The point at which any particular curve bends over (given by the line *OA*) is termed the *knee* of the curve.

Figure 8.16 shows the output characteristics for the common-base connection. It will be seen that the input current in this case is emitter current.

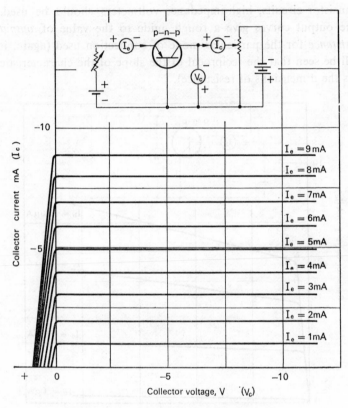

Fig. 8.16. A family of output characteristics for common base.

The output characteristics, in conjunction with a *load line*, are particularly useful in determining amplifier performance, and some aspects of this are treated in detail in § 10.9.

8.7. Collector leakage current

Figure 8.15 shows that a collector current flows even when the base current is zero. This is due mainly to thermally generated minority carriers and is, in fact, the reverse leakage current for the collector–base junction. In the transistor this current is termed the *collector leakage current*. For a low-power transistor in common-emitter, the leakage current is of the order 100–200 μA (at 25° C).

Leakage current also occurs with the common-base connection, but this typically is only of the order 5 μA (compared with the value for common-emitter quoted), and is too small to be apparent on the output characteristics shown in Fig. 8.16.

Leakage current is undesirable, especially in the common-emitter circuit, where it can increase rapidly with increase in temperature. This may lead to serious distortion of signals, and may cause damage to the transistor. Special circuits are required to stabilize against these changes, and are discussed in Chapter 10.

8.8. Simple equivalent circuit for a transistor

When a transistor is connected as part of a circuit the circuit is much easier to analyse if the transistor can be represented in terms of circuit components. Thus an *equivalent circuit* for the transistor is required. One type of circuit which is suggested by the actual connections to the transistor is the T-network shown in Fig. 8.17(a) for the common-base circuit. Part of the equivalent circuit is made up of resistors (which are *passive* components as described in Chapter 5), but because the transistor can amplify a signal the equivalent circuit must also contain an *active* component, i.e. a generator. The generator can be represented in many different ways, and a convenient representation is as a *voltage generator* in which the voltage is proportional to the input current. With common-base connection the input current is the emitter current and therefore the generator e.m.f. E can be written as

$$E = r_m i_e,$$

where r_m is the constant of proportionality. By Ohm's law, this constant must have the dimensions of *resistance*, hence the use of the letter r. Also, since the generator takes into account the effect of input current on the output circuit, it is a *mutual* link between input and output, and hence the subscript m. The other resistors in the circuit represent the physical properties of the transistor and are made up as follows.

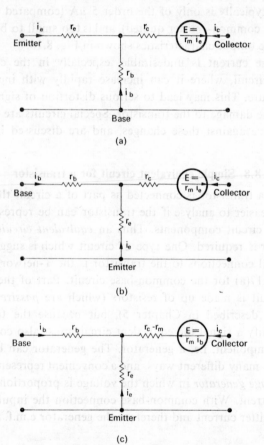

(a)

(b)

(c)

FIG. 8.17. (a) Equivalent voltage generator circuit for a transistor in common base. (b) The circuit of (a) arranged for common emitter. (c) The usual form of common-emitter equivalent voltage generator circuit.

r_e is the emitter resistance and takes into account the resistance of the emitter–base junction, the emitter ohmic resistance, and the effect of the depletion region in the emitter circuit.

r_c is the collector resistance and takes into account the resistance of the collector–base junction, the collector ohmic resistance, and the effect of the depletion region in the collector circuit.

r_b is the ohmic resistance of the base.

Figure 8.17(a) is the simple equivalent circuit for the *common-base* connection. When the transistor is connected as *common emitter* it is only necessary to interchange the emitter and base branches of the equivalent circuit to obtain the equivalent circuit for common emitter, and this is shown in Fig. 8.17(b). The disadvantage of this circuit is that the voltage generator is no longer a function of *input* current (now base current). This is easily altered since

$$i_e + i_b + i_c = 0$$

(remembering that the negative sign for current flow out of the transistor) is attached to the numerical value. Therefore

$$i_e = -i_b - i_c.$$

Hence
$$E = r_m i_e$$
$$= -r_m i_b - r_m i_c.$$

The first term in this expression is the equivalent voltage that is required since it is a function of input current, i.e. base current, and has the constant of proportionality r_m. The second term is an equivalent voltage drop across r_m, and can be represented by including a resistor $-r_m$ in the collector branch. The minus sign in front of r_m is necessary as shown by the equation. There is also a negative sign associated with the equivalent voltage, but this is taken into account by reversing the polarity of the generator as shown by the arrow reversal in Fig. 8.17(c).

A point which must be emphasized is that the circuits are only equivalent for *alternating currents*. For example, a short circuit could be placed across the output terminals of the equivalent circuit (collector–base terminals), whereas in practice this could not be done as it would short the collector battery.

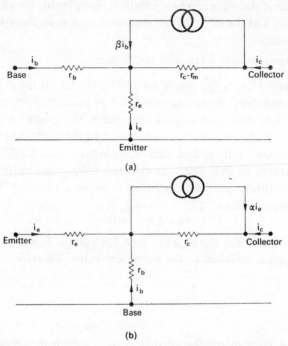

(a)

(b)

Fig. 8.18. (a) Equivalent constant current generator circuit for common emitter. (b) Equivalent constant current generator circuit for common base.

It is also possible to use a current generator instead of a voltage generator for the active element in the equivalent circuit, but, of course, both types of circuits must give identical results. The equivalent current generator circuit for the common-emitter connection is shown in Fig. 8.18(a) and for the common base in Fig. 8.18(b).

8.9. Limitations of the simple equivalent circuits

The equivalent T-circuits described have two serious limitations: (a) they do not take into account frequency effects such as capacitive current through the junctions, and (b) it is assumed that r_c, r_e, r_b, etc., remain constant, although in fact they alter with large applied signals. The equivalent circuits are therefore only useful for small-signal low-frequency analysis and must be limited to this.

8.10. High vacuum thermionic valves (vacuum tubes)

In a thermionic valve an electrode is heated sufficiently to emit electrons. These are collected by a second electrode, which is not heated, and therefore does not emit. Thus a one-way flow of electric current takes place. (Because of this one-way flow the name *valve* is used in the U.K.; in the U.S.A. the devices are termed *vacuum tubes,* or simply tubes, because the electrode assembly is usually mounted inside an evacuated glass tube.) The electrode which emits electrons is termed the *cathode,* and the electrode which collects the emitted electrons the *anode.* In the majority of valves, the passage of electrons from cathode to anode is through a near vacuum. Some valves, however, utilize gas in the conduction process, and these will be discussed in a later volume.

Cathodes

These may be made of various metals, and the efficiency with which emission takes place for a given metal is measured in terms of the energy which must be supplied (in the form of heat) in order to release electrons for conduction.

It is not possible to obtain an absolute vacuum in a valve, and the residual gases can combine with some metals to form a thin layer on the surface of the cathode which prevents emission. This is termed *poisoning of the cathode*, a condition which must be avoided. Another consideration is the melting point of the metal, which must be as high as possible. Of the pure metals, the best on all counts for use as cathodes is *tungsten,* and is invariably used.

The oxide-coated cathode

It has been found that by covering a pure metal cathode with a suitable oxide coating, an enormous increase in emission can be realized and at temperatures which are lower than those required for emission from pure metals. Practically all small power valves, e.g. those used in radio receivers, amplifiers, etc., have oxide-coated cathodes comprising a tungsten or nickel core covered with a thin layer of barium and strontium oxides.

The cathode may be *directly heated* in which case it consists of a filament of the cathode metal arranged as shown in Fig. 8.19(a). Battery-operated valves are nearly always directly heated

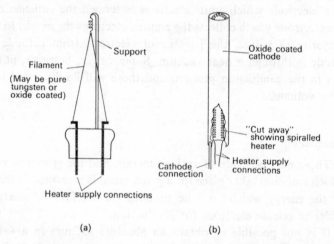

FIG. 8.19. (a) A directly heated cathode. (b) An indirectly heated cathode.

types. Alternatively, the cathode may be *indirectly heated*, in which case a filament of insulated tungsten wire is enclosed in a small sleeve of the cathode material, as shown in Fig. 8.19(b). This type of cathode is used where the heater is powered from alternating current. Its main advantage is that the cathode will heat to a steady average temperature, and thus the emission will be steady although supplied from an a.c. supply. In radio receivers, for example, this means that supply frequency "hum" will not be introduced through the heaters.

The anode

In the simplest type of valve (the diode), the anode surrounds the cathode and collects the electrons emitted by it. Under operating conditions the electrons may travel at high velocities and, on striking the anode, heat it. One of the problems in valve design is to keep the temperature rise of the anode within specified limits.

Anodes are usually made out of sheet nickel and are blackened to improve the heat radiation properties.

The vacuum

The vacuum is formed by firstly pumping out as much air and other gases as possible. During the pumping process the electrodes are raised to a high temperature in order to release any gases in the metal. Finally, a material, known as the *getter*, is evaporated by means of eddy currents, and absorbs any traces of gases remaining inside the valve. The evaporated getter deposits itself on the inside of the glass envelope, giving this its familiar silvered appearance. The gettering material is usually magnesium or barium, and it is positioned within the valve in such a way that as little as possible of it is deposited on the electrode assembly.

8.11. The diode

As already stated, the diode is the simplest form of valve. The word is a combination of *di*, from the Greek meaning *two*, and *ode*, the last syllable of electrode. The two electrodes are the anode and the cathode. (The heater and cathode assembly of

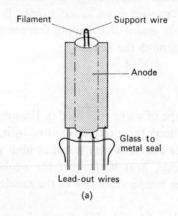

(a)

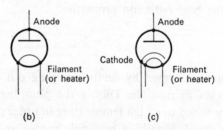

(b)   (c)

Fig. 8.20. (a) A typical diode assembly. (b) Circuit symbol for a directly heated diode. (c) Circuit symbol for an indirectly heated diode.

an indirectly heated valve is classed as *one* electrode.) A diode assembly is shown in Fig. 8.20(a) along with the conventional circuit symbols, Figs. 8.20(b) and (c).

A simple circuit, which enables the diode characteristic to be obtained, is shown in Fig. 8.21(a). As the anode voltage V_a is

increased, the anode current I_a increases as shown in Fig. 8.21(b).
It will be seen that at the higher anode voltages the current levels
off to a constant value. This is known as the *saturation current*.
It results when all the electrons emitted from the cathode reach
the anode, as further increase in V_a cannot produce more electrons. The value of saturation current can be increased by in-

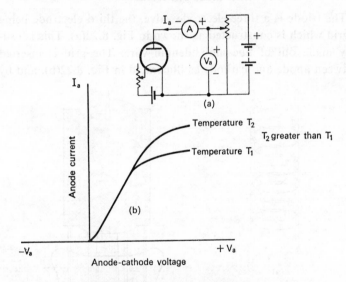

FIG. 8.21. The *I–V* curves for a diode.

creasing the cathode temperature. With oxide-coated cathodes the
saturation current is not reached in practice.

Below the saturation current region, not all the electrons
emitted by the cathode reach the anode, and those that do not
form a *space charge* between anode and cathode.

The curve shown in Fig. 8.21(b) is known as the *forward characteristic*. No reverse current flows in the thermionic diode when
the anode voltage is made negative, and in this respect the valve
diode is superior to the *p–n* junction diode.

It should be noted that the direction of electron flow is from cathode to anode, whereas conventional current flow as shown in Fig. 8.21(a) is from anode to cathode. Conventional current flow is always in the direction opposite to electron flow.

8.12. The triode

The triode is a three-electrode valve, the third electrode being a grid which is constructed as shown in Fig. 8.22(a). This is usually made out of fine molybdenum wire. The grid is inserted between anode and cathode as illustrated in Fig. 8.22(b), and by

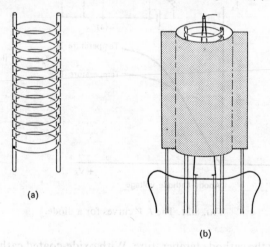

(a)

(b)

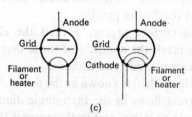

(c)

FIG. 8.22. (a) A control grid. (b) A triode assembly. (c) The circuit symbol for a triode.

applying a voltage between grid and cathode it is possible to control the current flowing to the anode. For this reason the grid is termed the *control grid*. The circuit symbol for a triode is shown in Fig. 8.22(c).

8.13. Static characteristic curves of a triode

Figure 8.23(a) shows a circuit which may be used to obtain the characteristic curves for a triode. Normally, a triode is oper-

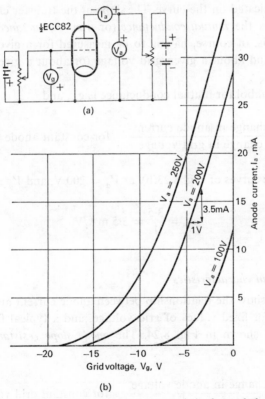

(a)

(b)

FIG. 8.23. A family of transfer characteristics for a triode.

ated in such a way that the grid does not draw current, and so it is not necessary to show an input characteristic.

The transfer characteristic

The transfer characteristic shows how anode current varies with grid voltage, and typical transfer characteristics for a triode are shown in Fig. 8.23(b). It will be seen that separate curves must be drawn for different values of anode voltage. For any one curve of Fig. 8.23(b), the anode voltage is held constant at the value indicated on the curve. The slope of the transfer characteristic gives the *mutual conductance* (or *trans-conductance)* of the valve, this, of course, having to be measured for a given anode voltage and about a given grid voltage (or about a given anode current).

The symbol for mutual conductance is g_m, and

$$g_m = \frac{\text{change in anode current}}{\text{change in grid voltage}} \quad \text{for constant anode voltage.}$$

From the curves of Fig. 8.23(b), at $V_a = 200$ V, and $V_g = -4$ V,

$$g_m = \frac{3 \cdot 5}{1} = 3 \cdot 5 \text{ mA/V}.$$

The output characteristics

These show the relationship between anode current and anode voltage for fixed values of grid voltage, and a typical family of curves is shown in Fig. 8.24. The *anode slope resistance r_a* is defined as

$$r_a = \frac{\text{change in anode voltage}}{\text{change in anode current}} \quad \text{for constant grid voltage.}$$

Thus r_a may be obtained from the output characteristics. For the curves shown in Fig. 8.24, for $V_g = -4$ V, and $V_a = 200$ V,

$$r_a = \frac{10}{1\cdot 4 \times 10^{-3}} = 7 \ \text{k}\Omega.$$

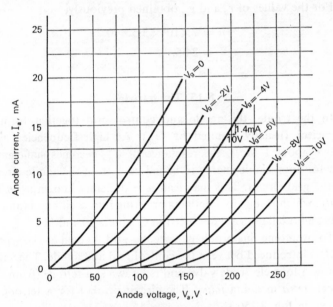

FIG. 8.24. A family of output characteristics for a triode.

8.14. The voltage amplification factor

The previous characteristics show that the anode current depends on both the anode voltage and on the grid voltage. It is thus possible to compare the change in grid voltage which just offsets a change in anode voltage to keep the anode current constant. The *voltage amplification factor* μ is defined as

$$\mu = \frac{\text{change in anode voltage}}{\text{change in grid voltage}} \quad \text{for constant anode current.}$$

The amplification factor may be obtained from either of the families of characteristics shown previously, but it will be shown in volume 2 that

$$\mu = g_m r_a.$$

For the values of r_a and g_m obtained previously,

$$\mu = 7 \times 10^3 \times 3 \cdot 5 \times 10^{-3}$$
$$= 24 \cdot 5.$$

8.15. The tetrode

In the triode, the anode and control grid together form a capacitor (usually denoted by C_{ag}). At high frequencies, e.g. above about 1 Mc/s, the reactance of C_{ag} becomes sufficiently low for appreciable energy to be fed back from the anode circuit to the grid circuit. This may lead to a difficulty known as *instability*, which results in amplifiers breaking into oscillation (amplifiers and oscillators are discussed in Chapters 10 and 11).

To overcome this problem, a second grid, known as the *screen grid*, is introduced between the control grid and anode. The valve is now a four-electrode valve and is known as a *tetrode* (from the Greek *tetra* meaning *four*). The circuit symbol for a tetrode is shown in Fig. 8.25(a).

The screen grid is connected to earth through a large capacitor known as a *screen-decoupling* capacitor. This is sufficiently large for its reactance to look like a short circuit to signal currents. Thus most of the signal current fed back from the anode flows through the screen grid and its decoupling capacitor to earth, in this way by-passing the control grid. The screen grid must be maintained at a positive potential with respect to the cathode, otherwise it would impede the flow of current from the cathode to the anode. It is therefore connected to the HT line through a resistance, this limiting the direct current which the screen takes. The circuit connections are shown in Fig. 8.25(b).

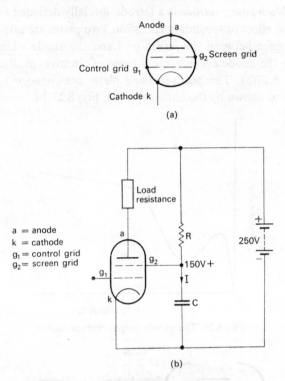

FIG. 8.25. The circuit connections for a tetrode.

The usefulness of the tetrode is limited by the fact that a "kink" occurs in the output characteristic, as shown in Fig. 8.26. This shows that over part of the curve the anode current actually decreases for an increase in anode voltage. The reason for this is that the electrons from the cathode, on striking the anode, knock out other electrons (termed *secondary electrons*), and over the range of anode voltage shown these are attracted to the screen grid rather than returning to the anode with a consequent reduction in anode current. Two methods may be used to overcome the effect of secondary emission.

The *beam power tetrode* is a tetrode specially designed to overcome the effect of secondary emission. Two plates are introduced in the space between the screen grid and the anode which concentrate the anode current into a *beam* of electrons as illustrated in Fig. 8.27(a). The beam-forming plates are connected to the cathode as shown by the circuit symbol, Fig. 8.27(b).

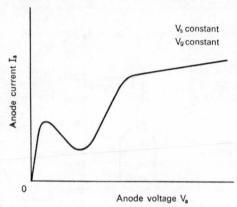

V_s constant
V_g constant

Anode current I_a

0

Anode voltage V_a

FIG. 8.26. The tetrode output characteristic.

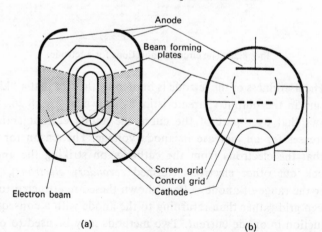

Anode

Beam forming plates

Screen grid
Control grid
Cathode

Electron beam

(a)   (b)

FIG. 8.27. The beam tetrode.

The concentration of electrons in the space between screen grid and anode creates a negative charge which repels the electrons back to the anode.

The chief advantage of the beam tetrode is that it can handle large amounts of power. However, it is limited to certain values of current and voltage, and a better solution to the problem of secondary emission is found in the *pentode*, discussed in the following section.

8.16. The pentode

The pentode is a five-electrode valve (the first syllable coming from the Greek *penta* meaning *five*). The fifth electrode is a grid

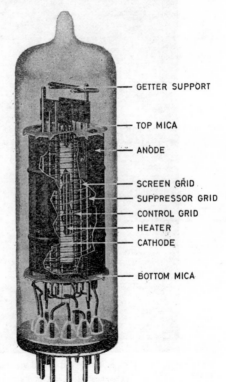

—— GETTER SUPPORT

—— TOP MICA

—— ANODE

—— SCREEN GRID
—— SUPPRESSOR GRID
—— CONTROL GRID
—— HEATER
—— CATHODE

—— BOTTOM MICA

Fig. 8.28. A pentode assembly.
(Courtesy Mullard Ltd. Valve type EL 84.)

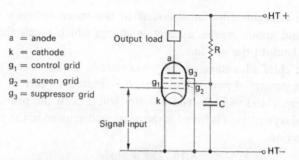

a = anode
k = cathode
g_1 = control grid
g_2 = screen grid
g_3 = suppressor grid

Output load

HT +

R

a

g_3

g_1

g_2

k

C

Signal input

HT−

FIG. 8.29. The circuit connections for a pentode.

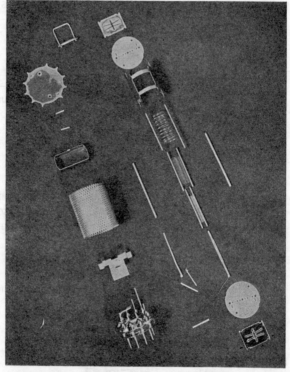

FIG. 8.30. An exploded view of a pentode.
(Courtesy Mullard Ltd. Valve type EF 86.)

termed the suppressor grid, and this is inserted between the screen grid and the anode for the purpose of preventing secondary emission electrons from reaching the screen grid. The suppressor grid is connected to cathode potential, and therefore repels electrons. The primary electrons (from the cathode) have sufficient velocity to overcome the repelling force, whereas the secondary electrons are returned to the anode.

The construction of a power pentode is illustrated in Fig. 8.28, and the circuit connections for a pentode are shown in Fig. 8.29. Fig. 8.30 shows an exploded view of an EF86 type pentode.

The pentode output characteristics

A family of output characteristics for a pentode is shown in Fig. 8.31, along with the appropriate circuit. It is apparent that for a wide range of anode voltage the anode current is almost independent of anode voltage. This is because the screen-grid potential produces the accelerating field which draws electrons away from the cathode (as in the tetrode), and a constant proportion of these pass through to the anode except at very low anode voltages. At very low anode voltages the behaviour is almost the same as for the tetrode, the important exception being that the secondary emission has been suppressed, i.e there is no kink in the characteristic.

As can be seen, the anode slope resistance of the pentode, given by the reciprocal of the slope of the output curve, is very high. Values greater that 1 M Ω are not uncommon.

The pentode transfer characteristic

Since the anode current is largely dependent on screen-grid voltage and not on anode voltage, a transfer characteristic must be obtained for each of several values of screen-grid voltage. Curves for only one value of anode voltage are necessary. Figure

8.32 shows a family of transfer characteristics along with the circuit used in obtaining these. It will be seen that the pentode transfer characteristics are very similar to those for a triode, but with screen-grid voltage replacing anode voltage as the third

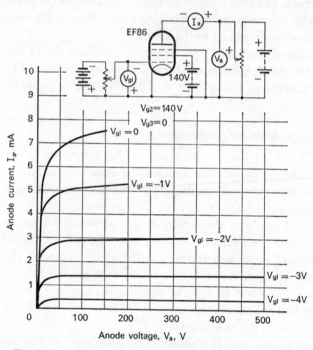

FIG. 8.31. A family of output characteristics for a pentode.

variable. As before, the slope of the transfer characteristic gives the mutual conductance for the valve. From the transfer characteristics shown, at

$$V_{g2} = 140 \text{ V}$$
$$V_{g1} = -2 \text{ V},$$
$$g_m = \frac{0 \cdot 8}{0 \cdot 4} = 2 \text{ mA/V}.$$

A very high voltage amplification factor is also possible with a pentode, and it is difficult to obtain a value for μ from the curves shown. However, the output resistance obtained from Fig. 8.31 is

$$r_a \simeq \frac{150}{0 \cdot 1 \times 10^{-3}} = 1 \cdot 5 \ \text{M}\Omega$$

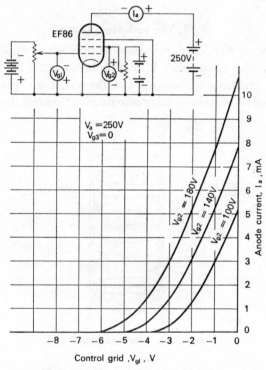

FIG. 8.32. A family of transfer characteristics for a pentode.

and using the relationship

$$\mu = g_m r_a = 2 \times 10^{-3} \times 1 \cdot 5 \times 10^6,$$

gives

$$\mu = 3000.$$

To summarize, the pentode valve was developed to overcome instability or the feedback problem which occurred between anode and grid in a triode. This was particularly necessary at radio frequencies. It was then found that the pentode also provided a high voltage amplification factor and a high output resistance. Thus the pentode is very widely used in amplifiers.

8.17. The variable-μ pentode

As already mentioned, pentodes find wide use at radio frequencies. At such frequencies it is difficult to control the amplification by conventional means, and the variable-μ pentode was developed to provide an electronic means of control. In this valve

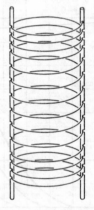

FIG. 8.33. A variable-μ control grid.

the actual amplification factor is reduced as the control grid is made more negative. This is achieved by winding the control grid so that the spacing between grid wires is close at the ends and widens out towards the middle of the grid (as shown in Fig. 8.33). The control exercised by the grid is greatest at the ends, and it is therefore the end sections which contribute to a high amplification factor. The centre section, being widely spaced, does not have the same degree of control on the anode current, and therefore the amplification factor of the centre section alone is not high. As the grid bias is decreased, i.e. made more negative, the portion of anode current through the end sections is gradually cut off, the current then being that through the centre, or low-μ section. Thus by varying the grid bias, μ can be altered.

8.18. Simple valve equivalent circuits

As with the transistor, the valve may be represented by a voltage or current generator, but because the grid is effectively an open circuit, the equivalent circuit is considerably simplified. The valve resistance for small signal changes is the anode slope resistance. Figure 8.34(a) shows the actual circuit for a triode valve and Fig. 8.34(b) an equivalent circuit. In this the battery is replaced by a short circuit since the circuit shows a.c. conditions only. The short circuit also means that the anode voltage remains constant. Therefore,

$$i_a = g_m v_g,$$

where i_a and v_g represent small alternating changes in anode current and grid voltage respectively. Applying Kirchhoff's laws to the loop of Fig. 8.34(b) gives

$$E = -i_a r_a$$
$$= -g_m r_a v_g.$$

This can be written as

$$E = -\mu v_g.$$

Thus the equivalent voltage generator circuit of the valve is as shown in Fig. 8.34(c). It may be noted that the minus sign in front of μ could be dropped if the direction of the arrow representing the polarity of E were reversed, but established practice seems to be to retain the minus sign and the polarity of E as shown. Another point which must be kept in mind is that v_g is the voltage of the grid *with respect to the cathode*.

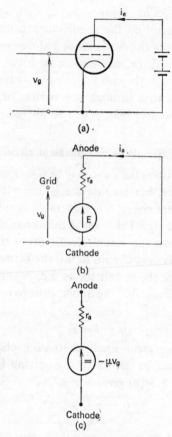

FIG. 8.34. (a) A triode circuit. (b) The equivalent voltage generator, stage 1. (c) The final form of the equivalent voltage generator.

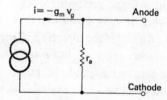

FIG. 8.35. The equivalent current generator for a valve.

An equivalent current generator circuit may be derived in a similar manner, and this is shown in Fig. 8.35.

8.19. Limitations of the equivalent circuits

The equivalent circuits do not take into account capacitive and inductive effects in the valve, which affect the frequency response. Therefore they are only useful for low-frequency work. Also, with large signals, g_m, r_a and μ tend to vary, which further limits the simple equivalent circuits to small signal analysis.

8.20. Worked examples

1. A milliammeter connected in the collector circuit of a transistor reads 3·0 mA, while a milliammeter in the base circuit reads 100 μA. Calculate the emitter current, and show, with the aid of circuit diagrams, the correct polarities of voltages and currents for the common base connection assuming (a) a p–n–p transistor, and (b) an n–p–n transistor.

$$I_e = 3+0\cdot1 \ \text{mA.}$$
$$= 3\cdot1 \ \text{mA.}$$

The polarities are shown in the circuits of Fig. 8.36.

2. For the circuit shown in Fig. 8.36(a) calculate the current amplification factor for d.c., assuming that the collector leakage

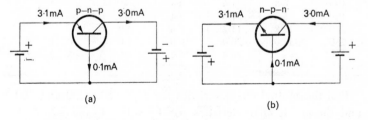

(a)   (b)

FIG. 8.36. In connection with example 1.

current is $5.0 \mu A$.

$$\text{Current amp factor} = \frac{3 - 0.005}{3.1}$$

$$\simeq 0.97.$$

3. Given that $\alpha = 0.97$ for a transistor, calculate, for a 0.1 mA change in emitter current (a) the change in collector current, (b) the change in base current, and (c) β.

(a) Change in collector current $= 0.97 \times 0.1$

$$= 0.097 \text{ mA}.$$

(b) Change in base current $\quad = 0.1 - 0.097$

$$= 3.0 \mu A.$$

(c) $\quad \beta = \dfrac{\alpha}{1-\alpha}$

$$= \frac{0.97}{1-0.97}$$

$$= 32.3.$$

4. Measurements made of a triode valve are as follows:

Anode (V) (V_a)	Anode current (mA)					
	$V_g = 0$ V	$V_g = -1$ V	$V_g = 2$ V	$V_g = -3$ V	$V_g = -4$ V	$V_g = -6$ V
100	8·8	3·6	0·8	–	–	–
150	15·2	7·6	2·4	0·4	–	–
200	22·8	13·2	5·6	2·0	–	–
250	32·0	20·0	10·0	5·0	2·0	–
300	–	26·8	16·7	9·0	4·8	0·4

Plot the mutual characteristics for $V_a = 200$, 250 and 300 V and the anode characteristics for $V_g = 0$, −1 and −2 V. Use these curves to determine the mutual conductance, anode slope resistance and the amplification factor of the valve over the straight part of its characteristics.   [C & G RLT A, 1961.]

Answer: The mutual characteristics are shown in Fig. 8.37 and the anode characteristics in Fig. 8.38. A suitable working point

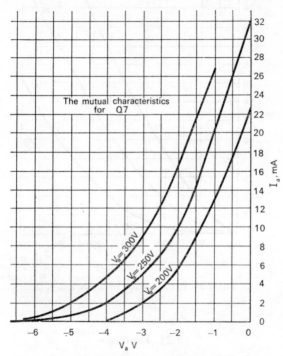

FIG. 8.37. In connection with example 4.

would be $V_a = 250$ V, $V_g = -1$ V. At this point:

from Fig. 8.37 $g_m = \dfrac{4 \cdot 4 \text{ mA}}{0 \cdot 4 \text{ V}} = \underline{11 \text{ mA/V}};$

from Fig 8·38 $r_a = \dfrac{20 \text{ V}}{2 \cdot 8 \text{ mA}} = \underline{7 \cdot 14 \text{ k}\Omega}$

and $\mu = g_m r_a = 11 \times 7 \cdot 14 = \underline{78 \cdot 5.}$

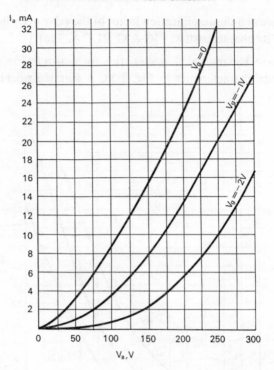

Fig. 8.38. In connection with example 4.

8.21. Exercises

1. Describe, in detail, a junction transistor suitable for use in an audio amplifier.

Sketch a typical family of characteristic curves for such a transistor when used in the common-emitter configuration. Scales must be clearly labelled. [C & G RLT A, 1962.]

2. By reference to the formation of a potential barrier and a current–voltage characteristic, explain the rectifying property of a *p–n* junction.   [C & G RLT A, 1961.]

3. Describe with the aid of sketches the construction and features of a low-power alloy junction transistor. Discuss the materials used.   [C & G RLT A, 1960.]

4. Describe with the aid of a sketch the constructional features of *either* a silicon *or* germanium crystal rectifier for use at very high frequencies. Quote a typical use for such a device. [C & G RLT A, 1959.]

5. Sketch sets of characteristic curves for the following:

(a) I_a against V_g for various values of V_a for a triode valve.
(b) I_a against V_a for various values of V_g for a pentode valve.
(c) I_c against V_c for various values of I_b for a transistor in the common-emitter connection.
(d) I_e against I_e for various values of V_c for a transistor in the common-base connection.

State what information may be derived from the slope of the straight portion of each of these curves. [C & G RLT A, 1963–4.]

6. Sketch sets of curves showing the following valve characteristics:

(a) I_a against V_a for various values of V_g for a triode valve.
(b) I_a against V_g for various values of V_a for a triode valve.
(c) I_a against V_a for various values of V_g for a pentode valve.
(d) I_a against V_g for various values of V_a for a pentode valve.

V_a = anode voltage, $\qquad$ I_s = anode current,
V_s = screen voltage, $\qquad$ V_g = grid voltage.

Explain, with reference to curve (b), what is meant by the term *mutual conductance*. [C & G RLT A, 1960.]

7. Discuss the shortcomings of triode valves and explain why pentode valves are commonly preferred to triodes in the high-frequency sections of medium-wave radio receivers. [C & G RLT A, 1960.]

8. Describe with the aid of a sketch the constructional features of an indirectly heated pentode valve. What factors determine the electron emission from the cathode?

How is a variable-μ characteristic obtained in such a valve? [C & G RLT A, 1962.]

9. By reference to a sketch explain the purpose of each of the three grids in a pentode valve.

Briefly discuss the reasons for using pentode valves rather than triode valves in the high-frequency stages of medium-wave radio receivers. [C & G RLT A, 1963–4.]

10. Describe with sketches the construction of *either* a beam tetrode valve suitable for use in the output stage of a domestic radio receiver, *or* a junction transistor suitable for use in a low-power audio amplifier.

Say what materials are used for the device you have described. [C & G RLT A, 1959.]

11. What is meant by (a) *the mutual conductance*, (b) *the anode a.c. resistance*, and (c) *the amplification factor* of a thermionic valve?

The following data were obtained for a triode valve:

Grid voltage (V_g)		0	−0·5	−1·0	−1·5	−2	−2·5
Anode	V_A 225 V	25	22·5	20	17·5	15	12·5
Current	V_A 200 V	20	17·5	15	12·5	10	7·5
I_A (mA)	V_A 175 V	15	12·5	10	7·5	5	2·5

Plot the I_A/V_g characteristic and determine the amplification factor, mutual conductance and anode a.c. resistance of the valve. [C & G RLT A, 1962–3.]

CHAPTER 9

RECTIFIER AND DEMODULATOR (DETECTOR) CIRCUITS

9.1. Introduction

The rectifying action of the diode (see Chapter 8) is made use of in *power-supply circuits*, which are used to provide d.c. from a.c.; and in *demodulator circuits (or detector circuits)* which are used to obtain the audio signal or other information signal from a modulated wave.

Power-supply circuits are often termed *rectifier circuits*. Although there is similarity in the rectifying action of rectifier and demodulator circuits, the applications of the two types of circuits differ sufficiently for them to be treated separately.

9.2. Power-supply circuits

A simple rectifier circuit is shown in Fig. 9.1(a). In this, R represents a load resistance (which may be the HT circuit of a radio receiver) through which d.c. only is required. The simple circuit suffers from two disadvantages: (a) the output voltage and current pulsates as shown in Fig. 9.1, i.e. consists of half-cycles, and (b) the mean value of output voltage or current is low.

The circuit can be considerably improved by connecting a capacitor across the load resistor R. If the capacitor is large enough, it will charge to almost the peak value of voltage. During the periods when the diode is not conducting, the load resistor R will partially discharge the capacitor. Nevertheless, the capacitor will hold the output voltage to a mean value which is considerably higher than that obtained in the simple circuit. At the same time, the pulsating effect is reduced because the voltage does not vary between such wide limits as in the previous case. The modified circuit is shown in Fig. 9.1(b) along with a sketch of output voltage. The added capacitor C is referred to as a *smoothing*

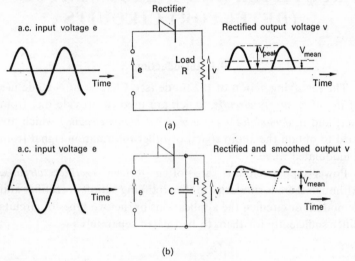

FIG. 9.1. (a) A simple rectifier circuit. (b) Smoothing added to the circuit of (a).

capacitor (or *reservoir* capacitor) and the output as a smoothed output.

The pulsating effect, or variation of output voltage about the mean value, is known as the *ripple voltage*.

In practice the ripple voltage must be reduced to negligible proportions. If, for example, ripple voltage is present on the HT to a receiver, it will be apparent as a hum in the output.

The ripple may be reduced by adding an inductor (or *choke*) in series with the output from the rectifier. This is known as a *choke-input filter* and is shown in Fig. 9.2(a). The inductor presents a high reactance which limits the ripple component of current, while the capacitor provides a low reactance path for the remaining ripple currents, thus by-passing these from the load.

The choke-input filter is found to have the advantage of providing an almost constant value of mean output voltage (e.g. the HT voltage) for load currents beyond a certain value. It is

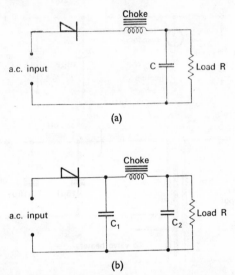

(a)

(b)

FIG. 9.2. (a) Rectifier with choke-input filter. (b) Rectifier with capacitor-input filter.

said to provide good *voltage regulation*. Its disadvantage is that the available output voltage is much less than that obtainable using capacitors.

The output voltage can be increased by incorporating a capacitor before the choke, as shown in Fig. 9.2(b). This circuit is known as a *capacitor-input filter*. The circuit provides a high value of output voltage as well as very good filtering or smoothing action. Its two main disadvantages are (a) it provides poorer regulation than the choke-input filter, and (b) the charging current for the input capacitor may be high enough to damage the recti-fier. The latter disadvantage can be avoided by careful choice of the input capacity C_1.

The circuits described so far are known as *half-wave* rectifier circuits because the rectifier only passes one-half of the input

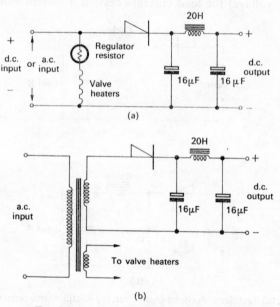

FIG. 9.3. Typical half-wave rectifier circuits.

wave. Typical half-wave rectifier circuits, and component values are shown in Fig. 9.3. The circuit of Fig. 9.3(a) can be used with a.c. or d.c. inputs provided the polarity of the d.c. input is as shown. This is an advantage where mains–battery operation is required. If the circuit is used to provide HT to a valve receiver, the valve heaters may be wired in series as shown, as this is the most convenient way of obtaining a low-voltage heater voltage for each valve from a high-voltage source. Where operation from a.c. only is required, the circuit of Fig. 9.3(b) may be used. This circuit has several advantages. (a) The transformer isolates the mains supply completely from the d.c. output, and therefore provides a safety factor, (b) valve heaters may be wired in parallel as a low-voltage supply may be obtained from the transformer, and (c) the output voltage can be increased by using a step-up transformer to supply the rectifier.

All half-wave rectifier circuits suffer from the disadvantage that they only operate on alternate half-cycles of input, and therefore the rectification efficiency is low. (The rectification efficiency is the ratio of d.c. output power to average input power and is low because the average output voltage tends to be low.)

Full-wave rectifier circuit

The situation can be improved by using what is known as a *full-wave rectifier circuit.* As will be shown, this circuit also allows for more efficient filtering, or reduction of ripple, and is therefore more widely used than the half-wave circuit.

Figure 9.4(a) shows a full-wave rectifier circuit utilizing metal rectifiers. The operation of the circuit is as follows. During the half-cycle that point *a* on the transformer is positive with respect to point *b*, rectifier 1 conducts and charges the filter capacitors. The return path for the charging current is through the centre tap on the secondary. During this period rectifier 2 does not conduct since it is biased in reverse.

On the following half-cycle point *b* is positive with respect to point *a*, and the situation is reversed. Rectifier 2 conducts and charges the capacitors with the *same polarity* of charging current as during the previous half-cycle. The return path is also through the centre tap. During this period rectifier 1 does not conduct.

Thus the capacitors are charged twice during each cycle of input current, and in this way the rectification efficiency is increased. Figure 9.5(a) shows the output voltage, and it will be seen that the ripple component occurs at *twice* the frequency of the

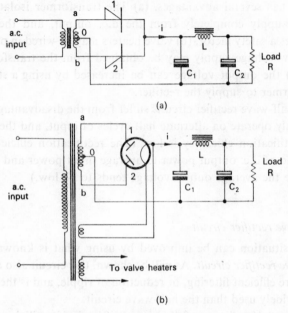

(a)

(b)

FIG. 9.4. Typical full-wave rectifier circuits.

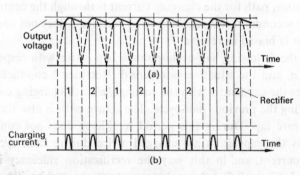

FIG. 9.5. (a) Output voltage waveform for the circuit of Fig. 9.4(a).
(b) Charging current waveform for circuit of Fig. 9.4(a).

supply (and therefore at twice the corresponding ripple in the half-wave circuit). Thus the reactance of the filter choke is twice what it would be in a half-wave circuit, and the reactances of the filter capacitors are one-half what they would be. The filter is therefore much more effective. The actual magnitude of the ripple is less with full-wave rectifier circuits compared with half-wave rectifier circuits. This is because the filter capacitors have less time in which to discharge between charging periods. Figure 9.5(b) shows the charging current for a full-wave rectifier circuit. The rectifier numbers shown in Fig. 9.5 refer to the rectifiers of Fig. 9.4(a), and shows their conducting periods.

In practice, rectifiers 1 and 2 may be assembled on the same stack. An alternative circuit, identical in action, but using a *double diode valve*, is shown in Fig. 9.4(b). The metal rectifiers 1 and 2 are replaced in this by diodes 1 and 2, these being in the same envelope. A directly heated valve is shown in the circuit, but in practice either an indirectly or a directly heated valve may be used. Typical values for the filter components are as before, namely, C_1 and C_2, 8–16 μF, and L of the order 10–30 H.

9.3. Demodulator (or detector) circuits

The purpose of a demodulator is to extract, or recover, the information signal from a modulated carrier wave. The circuit is essentially that of a half-wave rectifier circuit, but whereas the input frequency to the half-wave power supply may be of the order 50–60 c/s, that to the demodulator circuit may be of the order of many megacycles. Thus the values of the filter components are drastically different.

Figure 9.6(a) shows a very simple form of demodulator circuit along with typical filter and load values. The input voltage e is shown in Fig. 9.6(b) and the output voltage v in Fig. 9.6(c). As with the half-wave power rectifier, the capacitor is charged to almost the peak value of input voltage. Because the input frequency to the demodulator circuit is many times that in the power supply, the capacitor in the output circuit is much smaller than used in the power supply.

The mean value of output voltage follows the envelope of the modulated waveform and therefore represents the modulating or

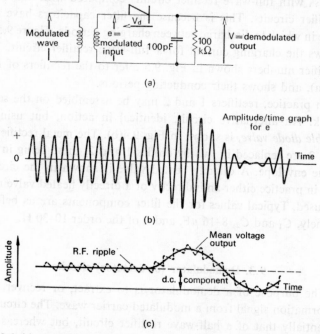

(a)

(b)

(c)

FIG. 9.6. (a) A simple demodulator circuit. (b) The modulated input voltage to (a). (c) The output voltage.

information signal. The output also contains two other components (a) an RF ripple, and (b) a d.c. component. The RF ripple must be filtered. The d.c. component must also be prevented from reaching the stage following the demodulator, otherwise it may act as an unwanted bias. This is easily achieved by means of a *blocking capacitor*, i.e. a capacitor which allows the a.c. component only to pass to the following stage. However, the d.c. component finds wide use in *automatic gain control* (a.g.c.) circuits.

Figure 9.7(a) shows a demodulator circuit suitable for use in a transistorized radio receiver. This employs a semiconductor diode. The load resistor R_1 also acts as a volume control. The

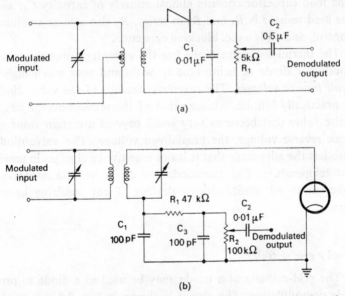

(a)

(b)

FIG. 9.7. (a) A demodulator circuit suitable for use in a transistorized receiver. (b) A demodulator circuit suitable for use in a valve receiver.

value of R_1 is considerably smaller than that of the corresponding component in the valve circuit [Fig. 9.7(b)], mainly because the input impedance of the following transistor stage is comparatively low. The value of C_1, the semiconductor diode load capacitor, is higher than that found in valve circuits, the high value being necessary to maintain a high rectification efficiency with low R_1. C_2 is a d.c. blocking capacitor.

Figure 9.7(b) shows a demodulator circuit suitable for use in valve receivers. Here it is found convenient to earth the cathode of the valve diode, and this is easily achieved as shown. It is also necessary to provide filtering for the RF ripple. The filter used is a capacitive input filter, the components being C_1, R_1 and C_3. R_1 is used instead of an RF choke because it is more economical to do so. However, it is less effective as a filter component. The load capacitor consists almost entirely of capacity C_1, and the load resistor is R_1 and R_2 in series. R_2 also acts as a volume control, and C_2 is a d.c. blocking capacitor.

The thermionic valve diode has the advantage over the semiconductor diode of being able to withstand very much higher *peak inverse voltages*. The reverse resistance of the valve diode is practically infinite, whereas that of the semiconductor has a finite value that becomes very small beyond a certain value of peak reverse voltage, the breakdown voltage. The valve diode also has the advantage that it is not sensitive to changes in ambient temperature. The semiconductor diode has the advantage inherent to all semiconductor devices of not requiring heater power.

Leaky grid detector

The grid-cathode of a triode may be used as a diode to provide demodulation. The circuit is shown in Fig. 9.8, where the capacitor C and the resistor R form the diode load circuit. (The name leaky grid comes from the fact that the resistor R allows the charge on the grid to "leak" sufficiently for the grid voltage to follow the modulation waveform.) The diode voltage is the grid-cathode input voltage, and the anode current will follow the mean variation, which is the modulating signal. An RF filter is included in the anode circuit to reduce ripple to negligible proportions. The output may be taken through a low-frequency transformer or through capacitive coupling as shown. This type of detector has the advantage that the triode provides amplification. Its chief disadvantage is that it distorts more readily than the diode detector. The mean input voltage must not exceed the cut-off voltage for the valve (see below), and hence the peak audio signal on the grid is limited to one-half the cut-off value if 100% sine wave modulation is considered. This will be apparent from a study of the input voltage curve v_{gk} of Fig. 9.8. It may be noted that this curve corresponds to the diode voltage v_d of Fig. 9.6(a).

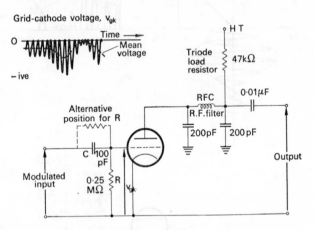

FIG. 9.8. The leaky-grid detector.

Anode bend detector

The transfer characteristics of a triode (Fig. 8.23) or of a pentode (Fig. 8.32) show that it is possible to bias a valve sufficiently to stop anode current flow. This is termed *cut-off bias*. Figure 9.9(a) illustrates the grid voltage and anode current waveforms when a modulated signal is applied to a valve biased to cut-off. As can be seen, the anode current only flows during positive half-cycles of input, and therefore the mean value represents the modulating waveform. Thus the output voltage across the triode load resistor represents the demodulated signal. As before,

an RF filter must be used to reduce ripple to negligible proportions. This type of detector [Fig. 9.9(b)] has a very high input
resistance which is usually an advantage.

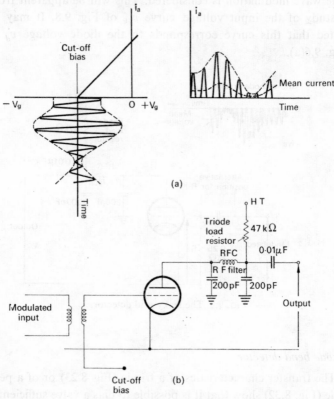

(a)

(b)

FIG. 9.9. (a) The action of the anode-bend detector. (b) Anode-bend detector
circuit.

9.4. Exercises

1. Explain the need for a detector in a radio receiver. Describe, with the
aid of a diagram, the operation of a semiconductor diode in the detection of
an amplitude-modulated wave. What are the relative merits of thermionic
and semiconductor diodes for this purpose?   [C & G RLT A, 1963–4.]

2. Draw circuits for the HT power supply of communication-type receivers using (a) half-wave, and (b) full-wave rectifiers. Indicate typical values of the smoothing components. Discuss briefly the advantages and disadvantages of each type of circuit.

If the half-wave rectifier were being used for a television broadcast receiver, what would be the advantage of using a selenium rectifier? [C & G RLT A, 1962–3.]

3. Draw a circuit diagram of an a.c. mains-operated power supply unit for a broadcast receiver. Give suitable values for the components, and briefly explain its operation. [C & G RLT A, 1962.]

4. Draw a circuit diagram and explain the operation of an a.c. mains power supply unit, suitable for transmission test equipment, such as a signal generator. What are the advantages of full-wave over half-wave rectification for such applications? [C & G RLT A, 1961.]

5. Briefly explain why it is necessary to include a detector stage in a receiver for amplitude-modulated signals. Discuss the characteristics of thermionic and semiconductor diodes which make them suitable for the detection of AM signals. [C & G RLT A, 1960.]

CHAPTER 10

AMPLIFIERS

10.1. Introduction

The amplifying action of valves and transistors depends on the fact that the input signal can exert control through the valve, or transistor, on the power taken from a d.c. source, which may be considerably greater than the input (signal) power. Depending on the application, amplification of voltage, current, or power, may be achieved.

10.2. Transistor amplifier circuits

The common-emitter circuit finds widest application as an amplifier, and Fig. 10.1 shows two simple CE circuits. In Fig. 10.1(a) a separate bias battery is required for each junction, whereas in Fig. 10.2(b) a single battery is used, the bias for the base–emitter junction being obtained through R_1.

The relationships between the various voltages and currents are shown in Fig. 10.2. To simplify discussion, values typical for a small-signal amplifier have been shown (although the graphs are not shown to scale). In Figs. 10.1 and 10.2 E = e.m.f. of collector bias battery ($= 4\cdot5$ V, the polarity being as shown), R_L = load resistor (5 kΩ typical), v_c = collector–emitter voltage, v_o = output signal voltage, e_s = e.m.f. of input signal source, R_s = internal resistance of signal source.

The circuit operation is as follows. When the signal e.m.f. e_s goes negative, examination of the polarities shows that it opposes the forward bias on the base–emitter junction. Thus, the emitter current is reduced, as shown in Fig. 10.2. Likewise, when e_s goes positive, i_e increases. The base and collector currents vary along

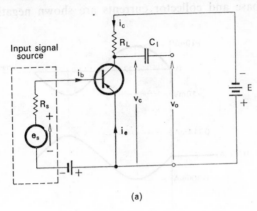

(a)

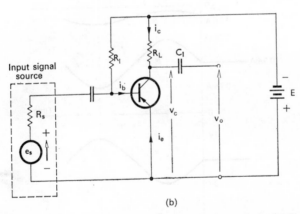

(b)

FIG. 10.1. (a) Common-emitter amplifier using two bias sources. (b) Common-emitter amplifier using a single bias source.

with emitter current, and always the emitter current is the sum of base and collector currents. This is shown by the i_b and i_c curves Fig. 10.2.

The voltage drop across the load resistor R_L is $i_c R_L$, and this must be subtracted from the steady voltage E, to give the collector voltage v_c, as shown.

The base and collector currents are shown negative in Fig.

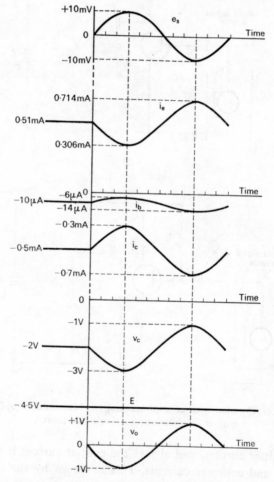

FIG. 10.2. The voltage and current waveforms for a CE circuit.

10.2, since by convention, currents flowing into the transistor are considered positive, and those flowing out as negative.

Generally, it is only the signal component of output voltage that is of interest, and thus a blocking capacitor, C, in Fig. 10.1 is used to prevent the d.c. component reaching the output. The resulting output voltage v_o is shown in Fig. 10.2 as a variation about zero.

Comparing the curve of v_o against e_s, it is seen that v_o goes negative as e_s goes positive, and vice versa. The voltages are said to be in *antiphase*. This is one of the features of the common-emitter circuit; it introduces a 180° phase shift between input and output voltages.

The common-base amplifier

A typical common-base circuit is shown in Fig. 10.3. Two bias batteries are required, and these are distinguished on circuits by the subscripts shown.

The relationships between currents and voltages are shown in Fig. 10.4. In this circuit, when the input signal voltage goes positive, the input current i_e increases. This is because the forward bias is increased. Taking this important difference into

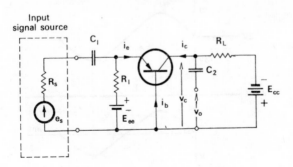

Fig. 10.3. A common-base amplifier.

account, the current and voltage curves can be constructed in a manner similar to that for the common emitter. It will be seen that the output voltage v_o is *in phase* with the input signal e.m.f., e_s.

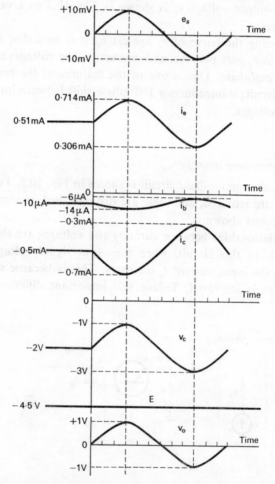

FIG. 10.4. The voltage and current waveforms for a CB circuit.

Comparison of common-base and common-emitter amplifiers

Table 10.1 summarizes the properties of the two types of circuit. The actual algebraic expressions for the input resistance, output resistance and gains will be derived in a later volume.

TABLE 10.1. COMPARISON OF COMMON-BASE AND COMMON-EMITTER
AMPLIFIERS

	Common base	Common emitter
Current gain	Approx. unity	High (e.g. 30)
Voltage gain	High (e.g. 40)	High (e.g. 70)
Voltage phase shift	Zero	180°
Input resistance	Low (e.g. 70 Ω)	Medium (e.g. 2000 Ω)
Output resistance	High (e.g. 600 kΩ)	Medium (e.g. 60 kΩ)

The medium values of input and output resistances of the common-emitter amplifier make it more generally useful as a circuit compared with the common base. Also, the combination of high current gain and high voltage gain results in a large power gain, this being a further advantage.

For some applications, the low input resistance of the common-base amplifier can be an advantage. For example, in *pre-amplifiers*, where the input is fed directly from a low-impedance microphone or pick-up, a higher power transfer is achieved as a result of the input resistance *matching* the source resistance.

Variation of gain with frequency has not been taken into account in the previous discussion. It can be shown that the common-base amplifier has a better frequency response than the common-emitter amplifier.

A further disadvantage of the common-emitter circuit is that the collector current is very temperature dependent. Changes of temperature can shift the operating point drastically, through changing the leakage current (see § 8.7). This must be compensated for in the common-emitter circuit, but is not troublesome in the common-base circuit. Compensating, or *stabilizing*, circuits are discussed in the next section. In spite of its disadvantages, the common-emitter circuit proves to be the most generally useful amplifier circuit at low frequencies.

10.3. D.c. stabilization

In the common-emitter connection, the leakage current increases rapidly with increase in temperature (above about 10°C), and this results in an unwanted increase in collector current. At lower temperatures direct variations of leakage current are negligible, but variations of r_e and β with temperature then become noticeable, which again result in unwanted variations in collector current. These unwanted variations of collector current with temperature must be compensated for in all but the most uncritical of circuit applications.

The most commonly used circuit which provides compensation is shown in Fig. 10.5. The stabilization and bias components are R_1, R_2, R_e and C_3. If the magnitude of collector current, and

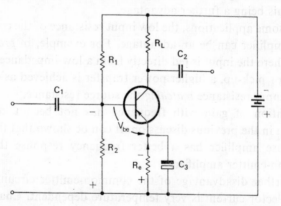

FIG. 10.5. D.c. stabilization by means of emitter resistance.

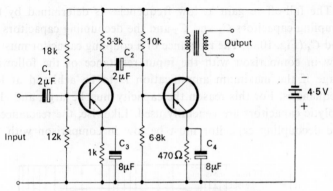

Fig. 10.6. A two-stage stabilized CE amplifier.

hence emitter current, increases, the voltage across R_e will increase. This decreases the forward bias applied to the base–emitter junction, which in turn tends to reduce the collector current.

The base current also decreases in magnitude, and this tends to increase the forward bias applied to the junction (less volts-drop across R_1), which would offset the compensating effect. To prevent this, the base voltage is held reasonably constant by means of the potential divider R_1, R_2.

C_3 is a decoupling capacitor which prevents signal voltage from appearing across R_e (an effect known as *signal feedback*).

A typical small signal, two-stage amplifier, employing compensation, is shown in Fig. 10.6.

10.4. Frequency response

The frequency response curve of an amplifier shows how the gain varies with frequency. At high frequencies, the fall-off in gain is due to the effect of internal capacities in the transistor, and also to the fall-off in the current amplification factor. Both effects are more pronounced in the common-emitter amplifier compared with the common-base amplifier.

The fall-off in gain at low frequencies is determined by the coupling capacitors C_1 and C_2 and the decoupling capacitors C_3 and C_4 (Fig. 10.6). The reactance of a coupling capacitor must be low in comparison with the input resistance of the following stage if the maximum amplification is to be achieved at low frequencies. For this reason the capacity must be large, and electrolytic capacitors are generally used. Likewise, the reactance of the decoupling capacitor must be low in comparison with the

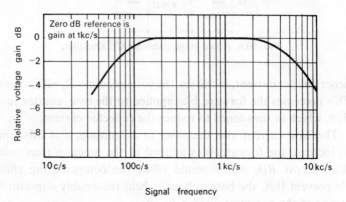

FIG. 10.7. Typical gain–frequency curve for a CE amplifier.

emitter resistance across which it is connected, and these are also electrolytic types. A typical relative gain–frequency response curve is illustrated in Fig. 10.7.

10.5. Valve amplifiers

The circuit for a simple triode amplifier is shown in Fig. 10.8 and the corresponding current and voltage curves in Fig. 10.9. Typical values are shown for a small-signal amplifier.

Referring to Fig. 10.8, C_1 and C_2 are d.c. blocking capacitors. C_1 prevents the grid bias (–4 V) from reaching the signal source, and C_2 prevents the HT at the anode from reaching the output terminals. R_1 is a high value resistor, of the order 0·5 MΩ, which prevents the bias source from short-circuiting the signal input.

As shown previously (§ 8.13), an increase in grid voltage increases the anode current. Thus, in the circuit of Fig. 10.8, when the signal voltage v_s goes positive, the anode current increases and the anode voltage decreases, since the voltage drop across

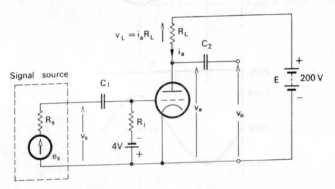

FIG. 10.8. A triode valve amplifier.

the load resistor $i_a R_L$ must be subtracted from E to give the anode voltage v_a. The voltage and current waveforms are shown in Fig. 10.9.

The output voltage v_o is the alternating component only of v_a, since capacitor C_2 blocks the d.c. component. It will be seen that v_o varies in *antiphase* with the input v_s (this is similar to the common-emitter transistor amplifier).

Figure 10.9 also shows the grid–cathode voltage waveform. It will be seen that the grid does not go positive, and therefore does not draw current.

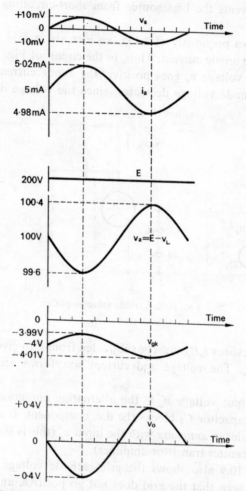

FIG. 10.9. The voltage and current waveforms for the triode amplifier.

Voltage gain of valve amplifier

The equivalent circuit of Fig. 8.34(c) may be used to replace the valve in Fig. 10.8 giving the equivalent amplifier circuit of Fig. 10.10. The voltage gain is defined as

$$A_v = v_o/v_s.$$

Applying Kirchhoff's second law to the circuit of Fig. 10.10 gives

$$-\mu v_s = -i_a(r_a + R_L),$$

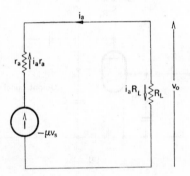

Fig. 10.10. Equivalent voltage generator circuit for the triode amplifier.

and from the circuit it is seen that the voltage across the load v_o is given by

$$v_o = -i_a R_L.$$

Substituting this in the previous equation gives

$$-\mu v_s = \frac{v_o(r_a + R_L)}{R_L}.$$

Therefore the voltage gain is

$$A_v = \frac{v_o}{v_s} = -\frac{\mu R_L}{(r_a + R_L)}.$$

The minus sign signifies the antiphase condition already discussed. A typical value of gain may be found using the values:

$$R_L = 20 \text{ k}\Omega,$$
$$r_a = 7 \text{ k}\Omega,$$
$$\mu = 25.$$

Then
$$A_v = -\frac{25 \times 20}{(7 + 20)}$$
$$= -18 \cdot 5.$$

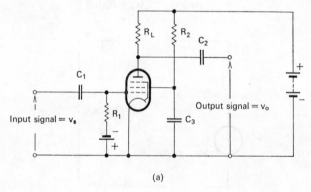

(a)

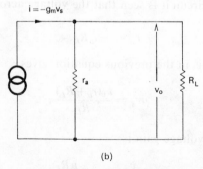

(b)

Fig. 10.11. (a) A pentode amplifier. (b) Equivalent current generator circuit for (a).

A pentode amplifier circuit is shown in Fig. 10.11(a), and the voltage gain for this may be found in exactly the same way as for the triode. With the pentode, however, it very often is the case that the load resistance R_L is much less than the anode slope resistance r_a. This condition may be written as

$$R_L \ll r_a.$$

The equivalent current generator of Fig. 8.35 then shows more clearly what happens in the circuit. The equivalent amplifier circuit using the current generator is shown in Fig. 10.11(b), and it is seen that if $R_L \ll r_a$, then r_a takes very little current compared with R_L, and the output voltage is

$$v_0 \simeq iR_L$$
$$\simeq -g_m v_s R_L.$$

Hence $A_v \simeq -g_m R_L.$

This, of course, is an approximate expression for the voltage gain.

10.6. Automatic (cathode) bias

Reference to Fig. 10.9 shows that i_a has a mean value, this being 5 mA for the typical values chosen. The mean value is the *direct current* component of anode current and can be used to

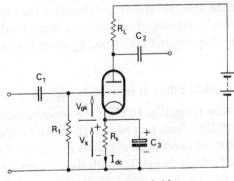

FIG. 10.12. Cathode bias.

develop a steady voltage for grid bias. This is achieved by including a resistor in the cathode circuit as shown in Fig. 10.12. The
direct voltage developed across this resistor R_k is

$$V_k = I_{dc}R_k.$$

The grid bias is V_{gk}, and since no direct current flows through
R_1 there is no voltage drop across R_1. Hence

$$V_{gk} = -V_k$$
$$= -I_{dc}R_k.$$

For example, if the mean current in the circuit of Fig. 10.8 is
5 mA and it is required to replace the 4 V bias battery with cathode
bias, then the value of bias resistor is

$$R_k = \frac{4}{5 \times 10^{-3}} \ \Omega$$

$$= 800 \ \Omega.$$

As before, R_1 must be large enough to prevent the input signal
from being short-circuited, and is usually of the order 100 kΩ to
1·0 MΩ. C_3 is necessary to prevent a component of signal voltage
from being developed across the cathode resistor R_k. Thus the
reactance of C_3 at the signal frequency must be small compared
with R_k. In audio-frequency amplifiers C_3 is usually an electrolytic capacitor of value 10–50 μF. Fortunately the working voltage
is low (4 V in the example given) and therefore the capacitor can
be small physically. At radio frequencies, a much smaller capacitance value is adequate and may typically be of the order 0·001–
0·01 μF.

10.7. Effect of input resistance R_1

As can be seen from Fig. 10.13(a) the input resistance of the
first stage (as distinct from that of the valve itself) is R_1. When an
amplifier consists of two stages, the input resistance of the second
stage (R_2) is effectively in parallel with the load resistance of the
first stage (at frequencies at which the reactance of the coupling

capacitor is negligible). This is shown in Fig. 10.13(b), where it is seen that the effective load resistance R'_{L1} is less than R_{L1}. Therefore the gain will be reduced. Often, the reduction in gain is not very much. For example let

$$R_{L1} = 20 \text{ k}\Omega$$

$$r_{a1} = 7 \text{ k}\Omega$$

$$\mu_1 = 25 \text{ } \lambda$$

$$R_2 = 100 \text{ k}\Omega.$$

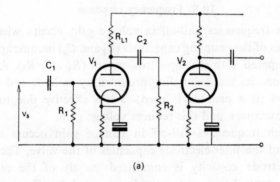

(a)

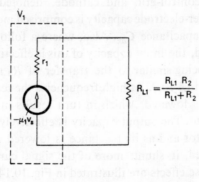

(b)

FIG. 10.13. Illustrating the effect of input resistance.

The voltage gain, not taking R_2 into account is

$$-\frac{\mu_1 . R_{L1}}{r_{a1} + R_{L1}}, \quad \text{i.e.} \quad A_v = -\frac{25 \times 20}{27},$$

$$= -18 \cdot 5.$$

Taking R_2 into account, $R'_{L1} = 16 \cdot 7 \text{ k}\Omega$.

Therefore $$A_v = -\frac{25 \times 16 \cdot 7}{23 \cdot 7},$$

$$= -17 \cdot 6.$$

10.8. Frequency response

At low frequencies, fall-off in voltage gain occurs when the reactances of the coupling capacitors (C_1 and C_2) become appreciable compared with the input resistances (R_1 and R_2). Also at low frequencies the decoupling provided by cathode and screen capacitors (if a pentode is used) is less effective due to their higher reactances, and this reduces voltage gain.

At high frequencies fall-off in voltage gain occurs mainly because of the inter-electrode capacities of the valve. The input inter-electrode capacity is comprised mostly of the capacity between control-grid and cathode, denoted by C_{gk}, and the output inter-electrode capacity is comprised mostly of the anode to cathode capacitance C_{ak}. Also, where a following stage must be considered, the input capacity of this is effectively in parallel with C_{ak}, this being similar to the transfer of R_2 across the load, as discussed in § 10.7. At high frequencies the reactance of the input capacity is lowered, which in turn results in attenuation of the signal input. The output capacity is effectively in parallel with the load resistor and as its reactance is lowered when the frequency is increased, it shunts more of the signal current away from the load. These effects are illustrated in Fig. 10.14. It will be seen that the frequency response curve is similar to that for the transistor amplifier (Fig. 10.7).

collector voltage is simply E. Thus a point may be found on the
output characteristics at which $I_c = E$ and $I_c = 0$. This is shown
as point x on Fig. 10.15.

A second point may be found at which there is effectively no
load resistance, i.e. R_L is zero. The load resistance
is tapped across the load resistance

$$I_c = \frac{E}{R_L} \quad \text{and} \quad I_c = 0 \quad E = I_c R_L$$

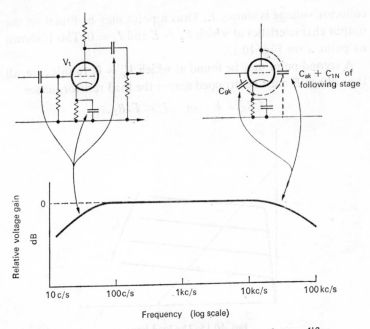

FIG. 10.14. Typical gain–frequency curve for a valve amplifier.

This point, given by $I_c = 0$ and $I_c = E/R_L$, is shown as y.
Joining these two points gives effectively the load line, so called
because the slope of the line characterises the load R_L. The value of the

10.9. The load line

The gain of an amplifier, and the power output in the case of
power amplifiers, may be determined using the output characteristics (see Chapter 8) in conjuction with a *load line*. The load
line is drawn across the output characteristics, and is a line which
takes into account the effect of load resistance. Its position on
the output characteristics is very easily determined. Consider, for
example, the amplifier circuit of Fig. 10.1, and let Fig. 10.15
represent the output characteristics of the transistor used. The
actual collector voltage is determined by the battery voltage E and
the voltage drop across the load resistor R_L. When the collector
current is zero, the voltage drop across R_L is zero, therefore the

collector voltage is simply E. Thus a point may be found on the output characteristics at which $V_c = E$ and $I_c = 0$. This is shown as point x on Fig. 10.15.

A second point may be found at which $V_c = 0$. In this case, all the voltage E must be dropped across the load resistor, hence

$$I_c R_L = E \quad \text{or} \quad I_c = E/R_L.$$

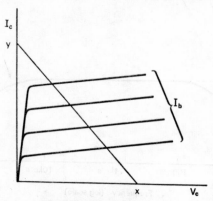

FIG. 10.15. The load line.

This point, given by $V_c = 0$ and $I_c = E/R_L$, is shown as y. Joining these two points together gives the *load line*, so called because the slope of the line is determined by R_L. The use of the load line is illustrated in the following examples.

EXAMPLE 1

Figure 10.16 shows the output characteristics for a common emitter amplifier for which

$$R_L = 1 \cdot 0 \text{ k}\Omega,$$
$$E = -9 \cdot 0 \text{ V}.$$

The load line may be drawn cutting the V_c axis at $9 \cdot 0$ V and the I_c axis at 9 V/1 kΩ = 9 mA. Let the base current be fixed by the bias at 100 μA, then A gives the *no-signal* or *quiescent* conditions for the amplifier. The values of collector current and collector voltage may be read off the axes corresponding to point A:

$$I_c = -4 \cdot 75 \text{ mA},$$

$$V_c = -4 \cdot 25 \text{ V}.$$

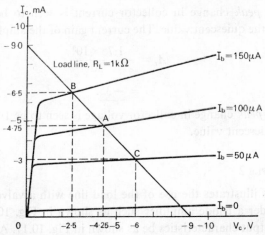

FIG. 10.16. Calculation of transistor amplifier gain using the load line.

Consider now a sinusoidal input signal to the base which has a *peak* value of 50 μA. The base current will rise to 150 μA and drop to 50 μA, and the corresponding values of collector voltage and collector current are obtained from points B and C. Thus, at $I_b = 150$ μA,

$$I_c = -6 \cdot 5 \text{ mA} \quad \text{and} \quad V_c = -2 \cdot 5 \text{ V}.$$

Therefore, for a change in base current of $+50$ μA, the collector current changes by

$$-6 \cdot 5 - (-4 \cdot 75)$$

$$= -1 \cdot 75 \text{ mA}.$$

At $I_b = 50 \, \mu A$,

$$I_c = -3 \cdot 0 \text{ mA} \quad \text{and} \quad V_c = -6 \cdot 0 \text{ V}.$$

Therefore, for a change in base current of $-50 \, \mu A$, the collector current changes by

$$-3 \cdot 0 - (-4 \cdot 75)$$
$$= 1 \cdot 75 \text{ mA}.$$

The *peak* change in collector current is seen to be $1 \cdot 75$ mA about the quiescent value. The current gain of the amplifier is

$$A_i = -\frac{1 \cdot 75 \times 10^3}{50}$$

$$= -35.$$

The *peak* change in collector voltage is seen to be $1 \cdot 75$ V about the quiescent value.

Example 2

This illustrates the use of the load line with a valve amplifier. Consider a triode amplifier such as shown in Fig. 10.8, and let the output characteristics be as shown in Fig. 10.17. Also for this example let

$$E = 240 \text{ V} \quad \text{and} \quad R_L = 12 \text{ k}\Omega.$$

The procedure is as for the transistor amplifier, with anode voltage replacing collector voltage, anode current replacing collector current, and the input being grid voltage.

Let the grid bias be $-4 \cdot 0$ V, then the quiescent conditions, as obtained from point A are

$$I_a = 7 \cdot 5 \text{ mA} \quad \text{and} \quad V_a = 150 \text{ V}.$$

With a sinusoidal input voltage of 2 V peak, the operating point on the load line swings up to B and down to C from which can be found, for $V_g = -2$ V,

$$I_a = 9 \cdot 0 \text{ mA} \quad \text{and} \quad V_a = 130 \text{ V}.$$

For $V_g = -6$ V

$$I_a = 6 \cdot 0 \text{ mA} \quad \text{and} \quad V_a = 170 \text{ V}.$$

Thus, for $+2 \cdot 0$ V *change* in grid voltage, the anode voltage changes by

$$130\text{--}150$$

$$= -20 \text{ V}.$$

For $-2 \cdot 0$ V *change* in grid voltage, the anode voltage changes by

$$170\text{--}150$$

$$= +20 \text{ V}.$$

It can be seen that a sinusoidal signal of $2 \cdot 0$ V peak on the grid gives rise to a sinusoidal anode voltage of 20 V peak. The voltage gain of the amplifier is

$$A_v = -\tfrac{20}{2}$$

$$= -10$$

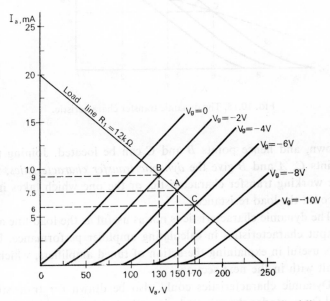

FIG. 10.17. Calculation of valve amplifier gain using the load line.

10.10. Dynamic characteristics

The effect of the load may be shown in another way. Consider first the transfer characteristics of triode valve shown in Fig. 10.18. Here the quiescent point is shown as A and, as before, this is given by $V_g = -4$ V, $V_a = 150$ V, and $I_a = 7.5$ mA. The static transfer characteristics for $V_a = 130$ V and $V_a = 170$ V are also

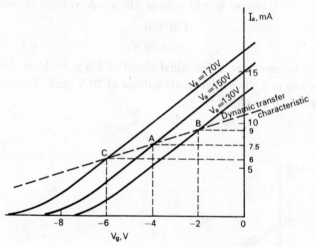

FIG. 10.18. The dynamic transfer characteristic.

shown, and hence points B and C can be located. Joining the points C, A and B give the *dynamic transfer characteristics*, i.e. the working transfer characteristic, or the one which takes into account the load resistance.

The dynamic characteristic is not as useful as the load line and output characteristics in calculating amplifier performance, but it is useful in explaining the action of tuned amplifiers, which is dealt with in the next section.

Dynamic characteristics could also be drawn for transistors and for pentodes. For these devices, the output current is almost independent of output voltage (see Chapter 8), therefore the static transfer characteristics are crowded close together, and the dynamic characteristic is almost the same as the static characteristics.

10.11. Tuned amplifiers

A tuned circuit may be used as an amplifier load, and this opens up a number of new possibilities especially at radio frequencies. The amplifiers may fall into one of three main classifications known as *class A*, *class B*, or *class C*. This classification is in fact perfectly general, and the amplifiers previously discussed are class A. However, the special features of class B and class C are particularily evident with tuned amplifiers.

Class A amplifiers

A class A amplifier may be defined as one in which the output current follows faithfully the input waveform. This is illustrated using the dynamic characteristic [Fig. 10.19(a), (b)]. Figure 10.19(a) shows the valve class A conditions and Fig 10.19(b) the transistor class A conditions, where, for simplicity, a common-emitter dynamic characteristic is used. In both cases, the output current waveform is obtained by projecting from the input waveform through the transfer characteristic. Thus, point *A* gives the quiescent values, point *B* the maximum peak values, and point *C* the minimum values. It may be noted that with class A operation, the mean power taken from the d.c. source is constant.

As already mentioned, the amplifiers discussed in the previous sections come into the class A category. When the load resistor is replaced by a tuned circuit, it is found that the amplification can be greatly increased, while maintaining class A (undistorted) conditions. Figure 10.20(a) shows the simplest form of tuned valve amplifier, the anode load being a parallel-tuned circuit. Figure 10.20(b) shows the selectivity of the amplifier, i.e. the manner in which the gains alters with frequency. The selectivity is usually quoted in terms of the 3 dB bandwidth (see § 6.4).

A pentode valve is normally used in simple tuned amplifiers in order to prevent unwanted feedback between input and output. When a transistor is used, some other method must be employed to cancel the feedback between output and input, and a common

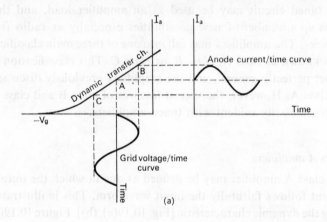

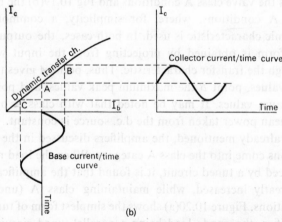

FIG. 10.19. (a) Class A operation for a valve. (b) Class A operation for a transistor.

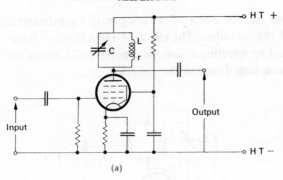

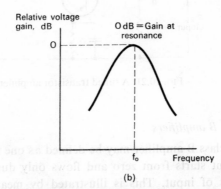

FIG. 10.20. (a) A tuned pentode amplifier. (b) The relative gain–frequency response curve

method is to *neutralize* the circuit. This means feeding back part of the output signal so that it is equal in magnitude but opposite in phase to the unwanted feedback, and thus the two cancel. One method of achieving this is shown in Fig. 10.21. By feeding back part of the signal through C_n, the *neutralizing capacitor*, the unwanted feedback through C_{cb} may be cancelled.

Figure 10.21 also shows that the output is taken from a tap on the coil. This is because in transistor amplifiers the input impedance of the following stage (i.e. the stage connected to the output) is low and has the effect of reducing both the gain and the selectivity of the amplifier. The effect of the following stage can be minimized by selecting a suitable tapping point on the coil rather than connecting direct to the collector.

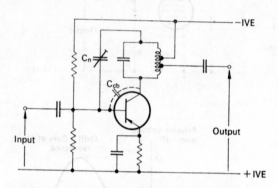

Fig. 10.21. A tuned transistor amplifier, class A.

Class B amplifiers

A class B amplifier may be defined as one in which the output current starts from zero and flows only during alternate half-cycles of input. This is illustrated by means of the dynamic characteristics (Fig. 10.22). Figure 10.22(a) refers to a valve and Fig. 10.22(b) to a common-emitter transistor circuit as before. In both cases the output current is seen to be a highly distorted version of the input waveform. However, the current waveform can be analysed into a *fundamental component* and its *harmonics*, just as the complex sound waves were analysed in § 3.3, and a circuit in the output, tuned to the fundamental component, will select this component for amplification.

The main advantage of the class B amplifier is that it has a higher power efficiency than the class A, that is, more of the input power (direct voltage × direct current to anode or collector) is converted to output power. The reason for the higher efficiency is that the output voltage is low when the current is high, hence the product, which represents the power dissipated, can be maintained at a low level. Also, during the half-cycle when the output voltage is high, the current is zero.

The tuned class B amplifier is used mainly in radio transmitter circuits. It is not as efficient as the class C amplifier described

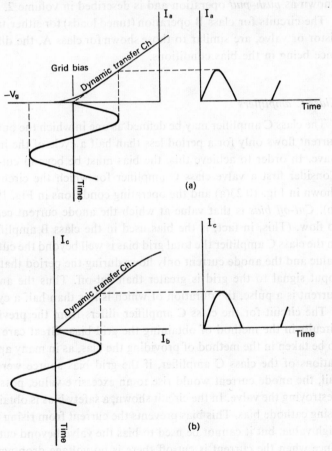

FIG 10.22. (a) Class B operation for a valve. (b) Class B operation for a transistor.

below, but it has an advantage that it can be used to amplify amplitude modulated waves. The class C amplifier cannot be used for this purpose.

The class B amplifier can also be used without a tuned circuit, but this requires two amplifiers connected in such a way that the half-cycles add to give a complete output waveform. This is known as *push–pull* operation and is described in volume 2.

The circuits for class B operation (tuned loads) for either transistor or valve, are similar to those shown for class A, the difference being in the bias conditions.

Class C amplifiers

The class C amplifier may be defined as one in which the output current flows only for a period less than half a cycle of the input wave. In order to achieve this, the bias must be beyond cut-off. Consider first a valve class C amplifier for which the circuit is shown in Fig. 10.23(a) and the operating conditions in Fig. 10.23 (b). *Cut-off bias* is that value at which the anode current ceases to flow. (This, in fact, is the bias used in the class B amplifier.) In the class C amplifier the total grid bias is well beyond the cut-off value and the anode current only flows during the period that the input signal to the grid is greater than cut-off. Thus the anode current is a pulse, the duration of which is less than half a cycle.

The circuit for the class C amplifier differs from the previous circuits in the method of obtaining the grid bias. Great care has to be taken in the method of providing the bias, as in many applications of the class C amplifier, if the grid bias source were to fail, the anode current would rise to an excessive value, possibly destroying the valve. In the circuit shown, a safety bias is obtained using cathode bias. This bias prevents the current from rising to a high value, but it cannot be used to bias the valve beyond cut-off since when the current is cut-off there is no voltage drop across the cathode resistor. The main bias is obtained by using the grid–cathode of the valve as a diode which rectifies part of the input signal in exactly the same manner as the diode detector described in § 9.3. (This is also similar to the *leaky grid detector* described in § 9.3.)

The rectified signal produces a negative voltage on the grid (which is the "diode anode") and this is the negative bias. It can be seen, however, that if the input signal were to fail for any

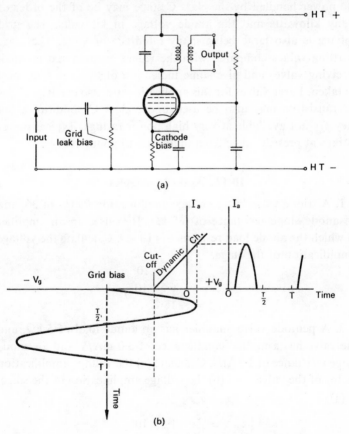

(a)

(b)

FIG. 10.23. (a) A class C valve amplifier. (b) Operating conditions for the class C valve amplifier.

reason, the bias would be removed with the possibility of the valve being damaged. Hence the need for the safety bias.

Class C valve amplifiers are used in the output stages of transmitters, and the tuned circuit selects the fundamental component of signal. The efficiency of this type of amplifier is very much higher than either the class A or class B, but the class C amplifier is limited to providing a sine-wave output. In large transmitters, the power handled by the class C stage may be of the order of many kilowatts and the anode voltage in kilovolts. The grid voltage is also large being many hundreds of volts. These are startling values compared with the values encountered in small receiving valves and give some indication of the care that must be taken. Large valves for this application are also costly.

Transistors may also be used under class C conditions, but they are not available at very high power ratings. Typical power ratings at present range from milliwatts to about 100 W.

10.12. Worked examples

1. A triode valve has a voltage amplification factor of 30, and an anode slope resistance of 6·5 kΩ. It is used in an amplifier in which the anode load resistance is 10 kΩ. Calculate the voltage amplification of the stage.

$$A_v = -\frac{30 \times 10}{6 \cdot 5 + 10}$$
$$= -18 \cdot 2.$$

2. A pentode valve amplifier has an anode load of 5 kΩ, and the valve has a mutual conductance of 3·0 mA/V and an anode slope resistance of 1·5 MΩ. Calculate (a) the voltage amplification factor of the valve, and (b) the voltage amplification of the stage.

(a)
$$\mu = g_m r_a$$
$$= \frac{3}{10^3} \times 1 \cdot 5 \times 10^6$$
$$= 4500.$$

(b) Since $r_a \gg R_L$,

$$A_v \simeq -g_m R_L$$

$$\simeq -\frac{3}{10^3} \times 5 \times 10^3$$

$$\simeq -15.$$

10.13. Exercises

1. Draw the circuit diagram of a two-stage RC-coupled audio-frequency amplifier using transistors. Show typical values for the components and suitable bias and stabilization arrangements. What factors influence the frequency response of the amplifier you have described? [C & G RLT A, 1962.]

2. Using the values given in worked example No. 4, § 8.20, draw the output characteristics for the valve, and on these draw the load line for an anode load of 8 kΩ, and an HT voltage of 275 V. From the curves determine the quiescent conditions (i.e. the mean, or d.c. values of anode voltage and current) for a grid voltage of $-1\cdot0$ V.

Assuming a sinusoidal voltage of $\pm1\cdot0$ V peak is now applied between grid and cathode, determine from the curves the approximate values for (a) the peak anode current swing about the mean value, and (b) the voltage amplification.

3. Data for a transistor are given in the accompanying table. From this plot the output characteristics for the common-emitter circuit and draw the load line for a load of $3\cdot9$ kΩ and a d.c. supply voltage of $12\cdot0$ V. Determine from the curves the quiescent conditions when the base current is 40 μA. Determine also the peak swing of collector current and collector voltage about the quiescent values, when the base current is varied sinusoidally by a peak value of ±20 μA about the 40 μA value.

V_{CE} (V)	1·0	2·5	5·0	7·5	10·0	12·5	15·0
I_c mA for $I_b = 20$ μA	0·5	0·6	0·75	0·9	1·0	1·15	1·25
I_c mA for $I_b = 40$ μA	1·38	1·45	1·65	1·8	2·0	–	–
I_c mA for $I_b = 60$ μA	2·3	2·4	2·6	2·8	–	–	–
I_c mA for $I_b = 80$ μA	3·3	3·4	3·6	–	–	–	–

CHAPTER 11

TUNED CIRCUIT OSCILLATORS

11.1. Introduction

In a resonant circuit, energy is continually alternating between magnetic energy in the magnetic field around the inductance and electric energy in the electric field stored in the capacitance. As the energy changes state it results in an electromagnetic wave, and thus alternating voltage and alternating current are both generated. Energy is also lost in the form of heat, in the circuit resistance and in the form of radiation. Even though these losses are kept very small, they result in the oscillation dying away to zero unless additional energy is injected into the circuit at regular intervals. One way of achieving this is to abstract a small amount of the circuit energy and feed it into an amplifier. The amplified output is then fed into the tuned circuit, and in this way continuous oscillation is maintained. The process is represented diagrammatically in Fig. 11.1. The *feedback path* is where the energy is abstracted from the tuned

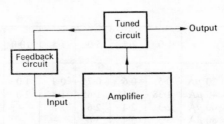

FIG. 11.1. Block diagram of a feedback oscillator.

circuit and fed back into the amplifier, while the tuned circuit may be the actual output load of the amplifier. Two essential conditions must be met for oscillations to be produced and maintained:

(a) The amplification must be sufficient to overcome the losses in the circuit.
(b) The overall phase shift must be zero around the loop, starting at the amplifier input–amplifier–feedback path— amplifier input.

A number of well-established circuits using either valves or transistors have been devised in which the above conditions are met, and these are discussed below.

11.2. The tuned-anode–tuned-grid oscillator

The circuit for this is shown in Fig. 11.2. In this the feedback circuit is simply the anode–grid capacity of the triode. The circuit values are usually arranged such that the tuned circuit in the grid determines the frequency of oscillation. In order to achieve the correct phase relationship, the tuned circuit in the

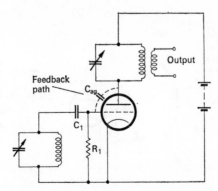

Fig. 11.2. Tuned-anode–tuned-grid oscillator.

anode must be inductive at the operating frequency. This is achieved by making it resonant at a frequency slightly lower than the operating frequency.

The grid bias for this oscillator (and for some of the other types described below) is obtained by the grid-leak method already described for the class C amplifier. The grid and cathode of the valve act as a diode and charges capacitor C_1. The polarity is such that the capacitor connection to the grid is negative thus providing negative bias. In order that the capacitor should not charge to too high a level, a discharge path is provided through R_1 and the d.c. path through the grid inductor. The output from the oscillator is usually transformer coupled from the anode load.

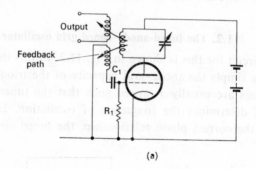

(a)

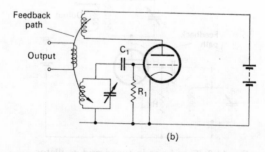

(b)

Fig. 11.3. (a) Tuned-anode oscillator. (b) Tuned-grid oscillator.

11.3. The tuned-anode oscillator

The circuit for this is shown in Fig. 11.3(a). The feedback path is through transformer (i.e. mutual inductance) coupling. The frequency of operation is determined mainly by the tuned circuit in the anode, but it is slightly higher than the resonant frequency of this circuit. The direction of winding of the feedback coil is important in determining the correct phase relationship.

11.4. Tuned-grid oscillator

This is very similar to the tuned-anode oscillator, the difference being that the tuned circuit is in the grid as shown in Fig. 11.3(b). This circuit is widely used in radio receivers.

11.5. The Colpitts valve oscillator

The circuit is shown in Fig. 11.4(a). The anode–cathode voltage is developed across C_a, part of the total tuning capacitance. This voltage induces an oscillatory current in the tuned circuit, and the feedback voltage is that developed across C_g (also part of the total tuning). The total tuning capacitance is C_a and C_g in series. The feedback path between anode and grid is the tuned circuit itself. That the correct phase relationship is obtained can be seen by considering the phase relationships existing in the tuned circuit, as shown in Fig. 11.4(b). When the anode a is going positive with respect to the cathode k, considering signal voltage only, the grid g is going negative with respect to the cathode. This is so because the opposite ends of the tuned circuit must be mutually in antiphase. Thus the grid–cathode voltage is in antiphase to the anodecathode voltage. Assuming that the valve produces a 180° phase shift, this will cancel the antiphase relationship, making the total phase shift around the loop zero. The actual phase relationship produced by the valve will depend on the anode load, but will be near enough to 180° for the zero-phase condition to be met. In fact, the operating frequency is slightly higher than the resonant frequency of the circuit, and thus the tuned circuit presents a slightly capacitive load to the valve.

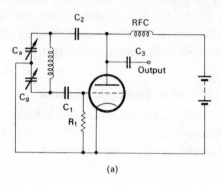

(a)

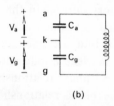

(b)

FIG. 11.4. (a) The Colpitts valve oscillator. (b) Phase relationships across the tuned circuit.

The circuit is termed a *shunt-fed* circuit because the d.c. to the valve flows in a separate parallel circuit to the a.c. circuit. The d.c. is prevented from flowing in the a.c. circuit by means of a blocking capacitor C_2, while the a.c. is prevented from flowing in the d.c. circuit by means of a radio-frequency choke (RFC), which offers a high impedance to the oscillatory current, but not to d.c.

11.6. The Hartley valve oscillator

This is similar to the Colpitts circuit but the feedback voltage is obtained by tapping the inductor rather than the capacitor.

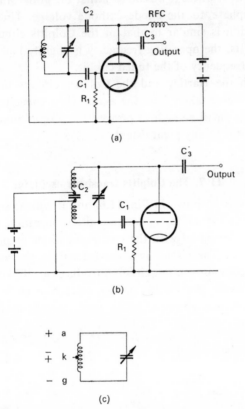

(a)

(b)

(c)

Fig. 11.5. (a) Hartley valve oscillator, shunt-fed. (b) Hartley valve oscillator, series-fed. (c) Phase relationships across the tuned circuit.

The circuit may either be shunt-fed, as shown in Fig. 11.5(a) or series-fed as in Fig. 11.5(b). In the series circuit the blocking capacitor C_2 is usually connected as shown to prevent the d.c. from reaching the grid components as well as from being short-circuited to cathode. This has the disadvantage that the coil in the tuned circuit must be split.

The phase relationships across the inductance will be as shown in Fig. 11.5(c) where it will be seen that the grid–cathode voltage is in antiphase to the anode–cathode voltage. Thus the mode of operation is similar to that of the Colpitts circuit. As with the Colpitts, the operating frequency is slightly higher than the resonant frequency of the tuned circuit.

In both the Hartley and the Colpitts circuits the output is shown as being taken from the anode via a capacitor C_3 which is generally small enough to prevent the output circuit affecting the oscillator to any great extent.

11.7. The Colpitts transistor oscillator

The circuit is shown in Fig. 11.6, and it will be seen that the transistor is biased for common-emitter operation (the circuit should be compared with the common-emitter amplifier circuit of Fig. 10.5. The circuit is shunt-fed as for the valve circuit. Since the common-emitter circuit introduces a 180° voltage phase shift, the same phase relationships exist here as for the valve circuit previously discussed.

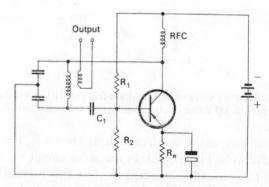

FIG. 11.6. The Colpitts transistor oscillator.

11.8. The Hartley transistor oscillator

The circuit is shown in Fig. 11.7, and again it will be seen that the common-emitter configuration is used. The base–emitter bias is obtained through the d.c. path of the tuned circuit, and R_1 and R_2. The capacitor C_1 provides the feedback path for the oscillatory signal, bypassing R_1. The same voltage phase relationships exist in this circuit as for the Hartley valve circuit.

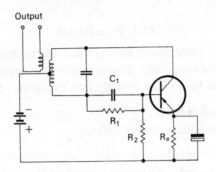

FIG. 11.7. The Hartley transistor oscillator.

11.9. Exercises

1. Draw the circuit of a simple medium-frequency LC oscillator using *either* a transistor *or* a triode valve. If such an oscillator has a fixed inductance of 60 μH and it is required to tune over the band 1 to 2 Mc/s, calculate the range of variable capacitor to be used.   [C & G RLT A, 1962 (part).]

2. Draw the circuit of an inductance–capacitance valve oscillator for use at 1200 kc/s, indicating suitable values for the components. Explain the purpose of the various components and the factors which determine their values.

CHAPTER 12

RADIO SYSTEMS

12.1. Introduction

The use of *radio waves* (or radiated electromagnetic waves) makes possible a wide and diverse range of communication services. These can be divided broadly into two groups:

(a) broadcast services;
(b) point-to-point communications.

Within these broad divisions there are numerous subdivisions. For example, broadcasting covers sound and television and standard frequency transmissions, while point-to-point includes telephone and telegraph services, fixed to mobile private communications systems, and radio links. Other services are radar and radio-navigational aids.

12.2 Sound broadcasting

A broadcast service is one in which information is transmitted for general use and serving as wide a population as possible. The sound broadcasting service provides the public with news, talks, music and other sound entertainment programmes. In many countries two types of service are available: (a) the national broadcasting service, which reaches the population of the country as a whole and (b) local broadcasting services which cater for local communities. Thus the programme material of the latter is limited to the interests of the particular community. Often the local service is a commercially operated enterprise, as, for example, in North America. In Britain, programme planners in the regional services may substitute a local programme in place of a national programme where this would be more in the interests of the particular region.

Programme material may originate from a number of different sources, and a *studio centre* should be able to control and select material from these various sources and pass it on to the transmitting station. Figure 12.1 shows the basic sections of a studio centre in a very simplified form. A distinction is usually made between a "live" broadcast and a recorded broadcast, and in Fig. 12.1, three "live" sources are shown. These are (a) the studio

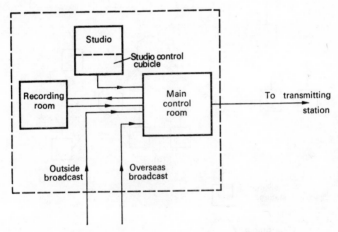

FIG. 12.1. A simplified block diagram of a studio centre.

itself, (b) the outside broadcast source, and (c) the overseas broadcast source. In the main control room, programme material can be selected and sent over lines to the transmitting station direct, or it can be selected for recording, in which case it is passed through to the recording room. From the main control room it is also possible to select recorded material from the recording room for broadcasting. It must be possible in the main control room to listen to all programmes that are being broadcast, and to check these for quality, time scheduling, and to give warning indications to studios when programmes are due to go on the air. These functions are usually carried out in a section known as the *continuity section*.

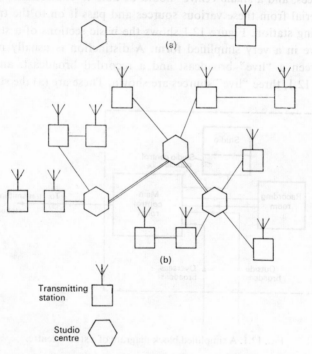

Transmitting station

Studio centre

FIG. 12.2. (a) A simple broadcasting chain. (b) A multiple-broadcasting chain permitting simultaneous broadcasting.

The broadcasting chain may consist simply of a studio centre and transmitting, as shown in Fig. 12.2(a), or, in the case of a national network, a number of studio centres may be connected together by telephone lines, and each centre in turn may feed a number of transmitting stations. This multiple station system is shown in block diagram form in Fig. 12.2(b) and permits what is known as *simultaneous broadcasting*, i.e. two or more transmitters broadcasting the same programme at the same time.

At one time all sound broadcasting services within any particular country operated on the *long wave* and *medium wave* bands. These bands together cover the frequency range of approximately 150 kc/s to 1·5 Mc/s. As the number of stations using this service increased, it was found that interference occurred between stations, although these might be situated far apart geographically. The interference results when the signal from the distant transmitter is reflected from a region high up in the earth's atmosphere known as the *ionosphere*, and it is found to be much more severe at night. Because of the crowding of stations in the medium wave band, the interference makes reception very unsatisfactory at night. Many countries have now instituted *very high frequency* (VHF) broadcasting services intended to provide high-quality programmes. This type of service is discussed briefly in the next paragraph. The long and medium wave broadcasting services continue to operate, and employ amplitude modulation with sidebands restricted to plus and minus 4·5 kc/s either side of carrier, i.e. a total bandwidth of 9 kc/s is required. Since the carrier separation in frequency in the medium wave band is 9 kc/s by international agreement, interference can also occur between stations situated in adjacent geographical regions. (One factor which helps to reduce the effect of interference is that the frequency response of the average domestic receiver is very limited, therefore it does not reproduce the high whistle which results when an interfering signal is present.)

The power transmitted in sound broadcasting may range from $\frac{1}{4}$ kW for small stations to 500 kW for large stations.

VHF broadcasting

This takes place in the frequency range 88–100 Mc/s, for which the range of propagation is limited to a little beyond the optical horizon (except under unusual and freak conditions). For this reason, interference between various stations seldom occurs. This type of broadcasting also utilizes a form of modulation known as *frequency modulation*, which can be used to give a signal almost free from noise and interference. (Frequency modulation is discussed in a later volume.) The broadcast service provided by this means is considered to be a high quality service.

Transmitted powers for VHF broadcasting may range from about 3 kW to 120 kW.

12.3. Television broadcasting

A television broadcasting chain will obviously be more complicated than a sound broadcasting system alone, since in the television chain both sound and vision make up the programme material. Not only must the studio cope with sound and vision, and co-ordinate these, but separate transmitters are required for each, as shown in Fig. 12.3.

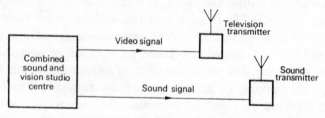

FIG. 12.3. A simple television broadcasting chain.

One of the main problems in television is the satisfactory tansmission of the vision signal. The vision signal alone occupies a bandwidth of many megacycles. The actual bandwidth depends on the actual system in use. In the British system, the vision bandwidth is about 3 Mc/s and in the American system about 4 Mc/s. If normal amplitude modulation were employed at the transmitter the radiated bandwidth would be twice these figures, which would be quite impracticable. In practice, a form of single sideband modulation, known as *vestigal sideband modulation* is employed in which most of one sideband is suppressed. A small remaining portion or "vestige" is transmitted with the other sideband and carrier, and helps to reduce distortion. It is obvious, however, that even with this reduced bandwidth, the transmitter could not operate in the medium wave band since the radiated bandwidth would be many times greater than the whole medium wave range. Television transmission therefore takes place at much higher frequencies in the range 41–76 Mc/s and higher. The bandwidth required for the complete transmission, including the sound channel, is 5 Mc/s in the British 405-line system.

Television services are also operated at higher frequencies in the VHF and UHF (ultra high-frequency) bands, the ranges allocated for this being 174–216 Mc/s and 470–890 Mc/s.

Another problem associated with television is the provision of *outside broadcast facilities*. With sound broadcasting, normal telephone lines can be used to get the programme material to the studio. With television this method cannot be used because the telephone lines are not capable of handling the wide bandwidth. Where outside broadcasts are likely to be a regular occurrence, as, for example, from a national sports stadium or from a concert hall, a permanent cable link, e.g. using high-frequency coaxial cables, may be made to the studio. In the normal situation the outside broadcast may originate practically anywhere within the country, and connection to the main television chain is then made through a radio link, operating in the microwave region. For example, in the British system, links are operating in the UHF range at 660 Mc/s, and in the SHF (super high-frequency) range at about 4600 Mc/s, and new SHF links on 7000 Mc/s are being introduced.

There are a limited number of points at which an outside broadcast contribution can be injected into the main programme chain going to the studio centre. Where the outside broadcast unit is a considerable distance from its nearest injection point, the radio link must be extended by means of a *repeater*, or *relay station*. This is shown diagrammatically in Fig. 12.4.

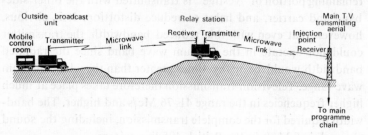

FIG. 12.4. A television outside broadcast link, using a relay station.

Colour television

The vision signal in colour television consists of a *luminance signal* and two *chrominance* signals. The luminance signal determines the brightness, or the distribution of black and white in the picture, and the chrominance signals carry the colour information. Each of these signals require a certain bandwidth, but it is found in practice that the chrominance signals can be transmitted in the *same* band as the luminance signal. Thus the bandwidth for a colour signal does not have to be increased over that for a black-and-white signal. The success of this method relies entirely on the fact that the eye cannot readily perceive the distortion which occurs with the luminance and chrominance signals overlapping.

12.4. Standard frequency broadcasts

Many countries transmit signals which are highly accurate in frequency and which can be used by anyone requiring a frequency (or time) standard. The standard frequencies, as agreed upon internationally, are 2·5, 5, 10, 15, 20, and 25 Mc/s. The British station (MSF) at Rugby also transmits a standard frequency at 60 kc/s.

In some countries the accuracy of the transmitted frequencies is as high as 2 parts in 10^{10} per day. This means that the frequency will not shift by more that ± 2 c/s in 10,000 Mc/s; or, for example, the standard frequency of 10 Mc/s will be accurate to

$$\pm 10 \times 10^6 \times \frac{2}{10^{10}}$$

$$= \pm 0 \cdot 002 \text{ c/s}.$$

In some cases the standard carriers are modulated by a highly accurate modulation tone. For example, the American station WWV modulates with a 440 c/s tone (the International music pitch A), accurate to 1 part in 10^8. Thus the modulation frequency error will be no greater than

$$\pm 440 \times \frac{1}{10^8}$$

$$= \pm 0 \cdot 0000044 \text{ c/s}.$$

Standard one-second time intervals are also broadcast, these being marked by short, highly accurate pulses of modulation.

12.5. Point-to-point radio services

Radio telephony is widely used as a means of connecting national telephone networks together, thus permitting international and overseas telephone calls to be made. The connections for a long-distance call of this type are shown in Fig. 12.5. The transmitting and receiving stations in each country are usually situated many miles apart, and different frequencies are used for transmit and receive. In this way, interference between the transmitted and received signals is avoided.

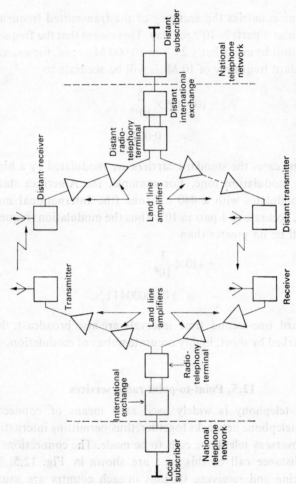

FIG. 12.5. Connections required for a long-distance radio-telephony call.
(*Reproduced by permission of H. M. Postmaster-General.*)

Before modulating the RF carrier, the speech signal is *scrambled* i.e. it is distorted in a special way so as to be unrecognizable as speech. At the receiving end, apparatus *descrambles* the signal, or turns it back into normal speech. This ensures a high degree of privacy, as, without the descrambling apparatus, the received message is unintelligible.

Mention has already been made of the *ionosphere* in connection with interference. In long-distance point-to-point radio services, the ionosphere is put to good use in reflecting the radio signal over the great distances involved. The frequency range best suited for this service is from about 3 Mc/s to 30 Mc/s.

Point-to-point circuits of the types described are also widely used in sparsely populated countries of large land area. In this situation, insufficient use may be made of the telephone to justify expensive cables or lines between communities, and the need for a telecommunications link is met economically by means of radio.

Radio relay links

A reliable, high-capacity telecommunications link may be established between two points using microwave links. The microwave link has a number of important advantages over the HF (ionospheric) links discussed in the previous section, the chief of which are:

(a) A wide bandwidth is available, permitting up to 960 telephone channels, or one complete television signal to be transmitted.

(b) Very high aerial gains can be achieved, allowing low transmit powers to be used. These are of the order 200 mW to 5 W.

(c) High reliability and freedom from fading is achieved through the use of "line of sight" paths.

Line-of-sight transmissions involve the use of *repeater* stations where long distances are to be covered, and in this respect the microwave link is at a disadvantage compared with the HF link. However, the microwave link represents the only alternative to cables (or waveguides) where wide band signals must be transmitted.

Point-to-point communications via satellites

Radio communication via satellite was first established when radio signals were transmitted between America and Britain using the moon as a reflector. Since then a number of reflecting type satellites have been launched in space, these being known as *passive* satellites. Other satellites, carrying transmitters and receivers have been launched, these being known as *active* satellites. Subsequent tests have shown that the active satellite offers the best means of obtaining high capacity, high quality communication links via satellites.

The path, or *orbit*, of the satellite around the earth is of importance. Of special interest is the *synchronous* orbit in which the satellite appears to be stationary above a given region of the earth. This occurs when the satellite is at a height of 36,000 km above the earth and rotates at the same rotational velocity as the earth from west to east in the earth's equatorial plane. Three satellites, equally spaced around a synchronous orbit, could provide a communications service between most regions of the earth.

One disadvantage with a synchronous satellite is that it takes a radio signal approximately a quarter of a second to complete the path from earth to satellite and back. Thus, on a direct telephone link, delays of about a half a second may occur, and tests have shown that delays of this order are undesirable.

The radio-frequency carriers used for satellite communication must be in the microwawe range, the optimum range being 1 to

10 Gc/s (or 1000 Mc/s to 10,000 Mc/s). These limits are mainly set by noise considerations. The satellite may be considered as a microwawe relay station. and proposed frequencies for transmitting from earth to satellite lie in the range 5925–6425 Mc/s and from satellite to earth in the range 3700–4200 Mc/s. In order to justify the cost of a satellite system, each satellite should be able to handle a thousand or more telephone channels and one television channel.

12.6. Fixed to mobile radio services

With this service, two-way radio communication may be established between a *base station* and a number of *mobile stations*.

Examples of services which require fixed to mobile communications are the police, hospital ambulance services, fire services, harbour control of shipping, taxi fleets, ground-to-air communications at air ports, etc. The main frequency bands allocated by international agreement for fixed to mobile service are 30–50 Mc/s, 148–174 Mc/s and 450–470 Mc/s. It will be seen that the radio carrier frequencies lie in the VHF or UHF bands, and therefore the range will be limited by the radio horizon, which is little further than the optical horizon. This range is limited by the aerial heights, and as the aerial height of the mobile station is itself limited in many instances, it is desirable to have the fixed station aerial as high as possible.

One of the major problems of this type of service has been that of providing a sufficient number of channels to satisfy the large number of users requiring the service. Originally the channel spacing was 100 kc/s (120 kc/s in the U.S.A.), but gradually this spacing was successively halved so that channel spacings of 12·5 kc/s (15 kc/s in the U.S.A.) are now being used. This represents about the limit of closeness that can be achieved, since the sidebands of one channel must be prevented from interfering with the adjacent channels. In turn, this imposes a very close frequency tolerance on the transmitters and receivers, these having to maintain their frequency of operation to within $\pm 0.0005\%$.

12.7. Worked examples

1. If the maximum frequency tolerance for fixed-service stations operating in the frequency band 4.0–27.5 Mc/s is ± 30 parts in 10^6 ($\pm 0.003\%$) and for television stations operating in the frequency band 40–70 Mc/s is 10 parts in 10^6 (0.001%), to what frequency variations in cycles per second do these tolerances correspond in the case of:

(a) a fixed-service station on 12.3 m, and

(b) a television station on 5.5 m?

At what wavelength does a fixed-service station, having a variation of ± 300 c/s, become outside the permitted tolerance? [C & G RLT A, 1959.]

(a)
$$12.3 \text{ m} = \frac{300 \times 10^6}{12.3} \quad \text{c/s}$$

$$= \frac{300}{12.3} \quad \text{Mc/s}$$

± 30 parts in 10^6 means ± 30 c/s for every Mc/s.

$$\text{Therefore tolerance} = \pm \frac{300}{12.3} \times 30$$

$$= \pm 732 \text{ c/s}.$$

(b) ± 10 parts in 10^6 means ± 10 c/s for every Mc/s.

$$\text{Therefore tolerance} = \pm \frac{300}{5.5} \times 10$$

$$= 545 \text{ c/s}.$$

A tolerance of ± 30 parts in 10^6 is the same as ± 300 in 10^7. Therefore the ± 300 c/s is outside tolerance when the frequency is less that 10^7 c/s or 10 Mc/s. This corresponds to a wavelength of 30 m.

2. Calculate the number the of fixed to mobile channels which may be accommodated in the 148–174 Mc/s band, assuming 25 kc/s spacing between channels.

$$\text{No. of channels} = \frac{(174-148) \times 1000}{25}$$

$$= \underline{1040}.$$

3. (a) Assuming that transmission occurs on a VHF channel on 160 Mc/s, the highest modulating frequency being 3 kc/s, and that the adjacent channels spaced 25 kc/s either side are on receive, sketch the bandwidths occupied by each channel. Assume that the receive channels have a bandwidth flat to $\pm 4\cdot5$ kc/s.

(b) Sketch also the bandwidth for the 160 Mc/s channel and its upper adjacent channel, when the 160 Mc/s channel is transmitting on the $+0\cdot0005\%$ limit of its frequency tolerance, and the adjacent channel is receiving on its $-0\cdot0005\%$ limit. Show the relative positions of the transmit and receive bandwidths for the 160 Mc/s channel, assuming that the receiver remains accurately on frequency.

(a) See Fig. 12.6(a).

(b) $0\cdot0005\%$ means 5 parts in 10^6.

Therefore at 160 Mc/s, carrier shift $= +160 \times 5$ c/s
$$= 800 \text{ c/s},$$

and at $160\cdot025$ Mc/s, shift $\simeq -800$ c/s.

The bandwidths are as shown in Fig. 12.6(b).

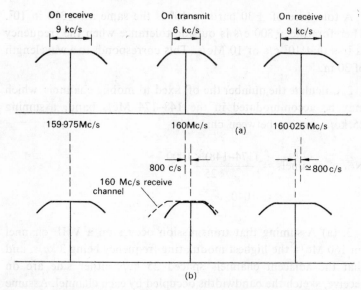

FIG. 12.6. (a) Answer to Example 3(a). (b) Answer to Example 3(b).

12.8. Exercises

1. State the approximate values of carrier frequencies you would expect to find used for the following applications:

(a) a high-quality sound broadcast service to serve a relatively small area;
(b) a point-to-point television radio-relay system.

[C & G RLT A, 1960, part.]

2. Draw suitably annotated block schematic diagrams of the following simple line and radio communication systems:

(a) Connections required for an overseas radio-telephone call between two subscribers on different continents.
(b) Connections required for a multistation broadcast from an outside broadcast event.
(c) Connections required for an overseas radio-telegraphy call between a shipping company and one of its ships.

[C & G RLT A, 1963–4.]

3. With the aid of a block diagram explain the connections required for an overseas radio-telephone call between a subscriber on a remote island in one continent and a subscriber in another continent.

Suggest suitable carrier frequencies which might be used on the national telephone network and the international radio circuits involved. [C & G RLT A, 1962.]

CHAPTER 13

LINE TELEPHONY

13.1. Introduction

The word *telephone* is made up of two Greek words, *tele* meaning *far*, and *phone* meaning *voice*. Today the word means especially the transmission of speech to a distance by means of electricity, a telephone conversation being an example of this. Telephony, therefore, is the branch of electrical communications which deals with the transmission of speech directly without the use of codes.

When the message is sent over wire lines, the method of transmission is termed *line telephony*, and when radio transmission is employed, it is known as *radio telephony*. On many overseas telephone calls, both radio and line transmission methods are used together in the communications link.

Where only a single speech circuit is required, the lines need only be capable of handling frequencies of 300–3400 c/s. In many cases a number of speech channels have to be provided and then the individual speech bands are modulated onto separate carriers. The line-carrier frequencies may range from about 6 kc/s to 3 Mc/s depending on the number of channels required.

13.2 Telephony circuits

Figure 13.1 shows a simple line telephone system. In line communications the microphone is referred to as the transmitter, and is invariably a carbon-granule type microphone. The receiver is nearly always a permanent magnet moving diaphragm type. The principles of operation of both transmitter and receiver are discussed in Chapter 7. The battery supplies the current for the microphone. A switch is provided at each end, which in its off position connects the receivers to the line, and which must be operated to switch in the transmitters. It is obvious that transmission can only take place in one direction at a time; this is known as *simplex* operation.

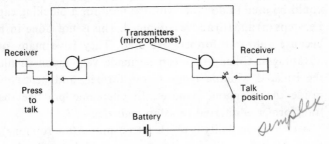

FIG. 13.1. A simple telephone system.

Apart from the social consequences of not allowing one party to interrupt the other, the system has the following technical drawbacks:

(a) The d.c. required for the microphone also flows through the receiver. This may result in demagnetization of the permanent magnets.

(b) No attempt is made to achieve maximum transfer of power from transmitter to line, and from line to receiver.

(c) The magnitude of the direct current to the microphone is dependent on the length of line. Hence, for a given battery voltage, the maximum possible output available from the transmitter will decrease as the length of line increases.

In modern telephone networks the steps taken to overcome these disadvantages are:

(a) A capacitor is used to block the direct current from the receiver circuit.

(b) Transformers are used to improve the efficiency of power transfer.

(c) The effect of line resistance is minimized by using either a local battery system or a central battery system. Both systems are discussed below.

It might be thought that the isolating property of a transformer could be used to do away with the need for a blocking capacitor, i.e. steps (a) and (b) above combined. This is not done in practice because auto-transformers are used. They have many practical advantages. Chiefly they can be made very much smaller than the isolated winding type of transformer, and hence mounted inside the telephone handset. In telephone practice the auto-transformer is referred to as an *induction coil*.

Another possibility is to use a transmitter (microphone), which does not require direct current, e.g. a moving-coil microphone. Again, the practical advantages of the carbon microphone make it more attractive than any other type. Its power output is high, it is moderate in cost and it is robust.

Figure 13.2 shows the modified circuit incorporating the blocking capacitors and induction coils. This circuit also illustrates the *local battery system*, of connection.

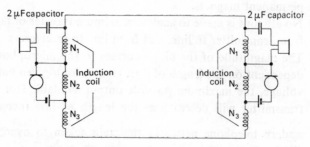

FIG. 13.2. An improved version of Fig. 13.1.

Local battery system

Each transmitter is supplied with its own battery. The transmitter primary winding N_2 is low resistance, and hence the d.c. is localized to the loop containing battery, transmitter and winding N_2. It is, therefore, unaffected by length of line. The battery maintanence problem with this system is an obvious disadvantage. It is only used in special situations such as point-to-point links, small local networks in remote areas and where line resistance is exceptionally high.

The induction coil presents to the line a total winding of $N_1+N_2+N_3$; to the transmitter a winding N_2; and to the receiver a winding N_1. The transmitter is therefore connected to the line through a voltage step-up transformer of turns ratio,

$$\frac{N_1+N_2+N_3}{N_2}.$$

The receiver is fed from the line through a voltage step-down transformer of turns ratio,

$$\frac{N_1}{N_1+N_2+N_3}.$$

Typical values for the windings are:

N_1	1000 turns	17 Ω resistance
N_2	400 turns	1 Ω resistance
N_3	1500 turns	33 Ω resistance

A complete telephone network must, of course, include dialling (or signalling) facilities, but such details are outside the scope of this book.

It will be seen that with the circuit of Fig. 13.2 a press-to-talk switch is not required, transmission being possible in both directions simultaneously. This is known as *duplex* operation.

Central battery system

In large nationwide telephone networks it is not feasible to provide a battery for every transmitter. Instead, one large capacity battery is provided at the telephone exchange and is connected in parallel with the line through a voice frequency impedance.

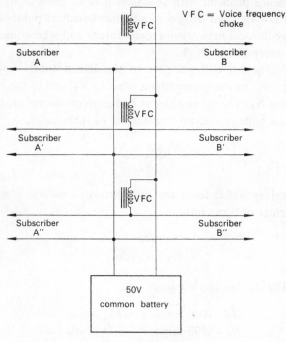

FIG. 13.3. Central battery supply.

Figure 13.3 shows how three separate circuits may use the same battery. The battery supplies current to all the lines through the voice frequency chokes. These offer very low impedance to direct currents and high impedance to current at audio frequencies; therefore they prevent the speech currents on each line from being short circuited by the battery and from transferring from one line onto another. The audio-frequency choke provides a common impedance for the speech currents of subscribers A and B or, in effect, bridges the lines from one subscriber to the other. It is therefore termed a *transmission bridge*. Very often in practice the choke consists of the winding of one of the relays used in the signalling circuit.

13.3. Transmission bridges

The transmission bridge may consist of a simple audio-frequency choke as already discussed and Fig. 13.4 illustrates this in more detail. Figure 13.4(a) shows the d.c. paths for the system, and Fig. 13.4(b) the speech current paths. A two-winding induc-

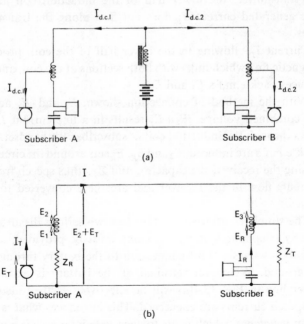

(a)

(b)

FIG. 13.4. (a) D.c. paths in a simple transmission bridge. (b) Speech current paths.

tion coil is used, and the turns ratio is chosen to be reasonably satisfactory for both transmission and reception, although not the optimum for either. Assuming that both subscriber circuits offer roughly the same d.c. resistance to the central battery, the d.c. will divide evenly between the circuits. Thus each transmitter will operate at about the same output. Consider now the circuit shown in Fig. 13.4(b) which shows subscriber A transmitting and subscriber B receiving. For convenience, the receiver at subscriber A's handset is shown as an impedance Z_R and the transmitter at subscriber B's handset as an impedance Z_T. When sound waves impinge on the transmitter at A they result in a voltage E_T being generated. This in turn results in a current I_T which is almost completely localized to the low-impedance circuit consisting of the transmitter, the lower half of the induction coil and Z_R. The generated current I_T does not flow along the transmission lines.

Current I_T, flowing in the lower half of the coil, produces a magnetic flux which links with both sections of the coil, and hence induces back e.m.f.s E_1 and E_2.

With the method of connection shown, E_2 and E_T add, and the combined voltage, E_2+E_T results in a line current I, which flows through the induction coil at subscriber B's handset. Again, back e.m.f.s are induced, E_3 and E_R. E_R acts around the circuit comprising the receiver, the capacitor and Z_T; thus speech frequency currents flow in the receiver and are there converted to sound waves.

The simple transmission bridge has two serious disadvantages. In any telephone system, signalling must be provided, and this usually involves a third connection to the battery through earth or ground. Whichever terminal of the battery is earthed, the lower line in Fig. 13.4(a) will be effectively earthed also as far as speech currents are concerned. This introduces what is known as an *unbalance*, which tends to aggravate interference and crosstalk. Secondly, successful operation of the circuit depends on the d.c. dividing more or less evenly between the subscribers. This is not a problem in small private installations (e.g. the installation in large buildings), but is a problem in the large public systems where line resistance may vary between wide limits. Various bridges have been designed to overcome both difficulties, one example being the *Stone transmission bridge* shown in Fig. 13.5.

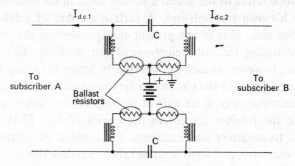

FIG. 13.5. The Stone transmission bridge.

The single choke in the previous case is replaced by four chokes, two in the positive side and two in the negative side. Thus each line is completely isolated from earth as far as speech currents are concerned. The direct currents can now be adjusted independently of each other (I_{dc1} and I_{dc2} in Fig. 13.5). This adjustment is usually carried out automatically by means of *ballast resistors* connected in each line. A ballast resistor (sometimes called a *barretter*) is a resistor made of material having a high positive temperature coefficient of resistance. If a large current tends to flow, the heat generated in the ballast resistor increases the resistance, thus limiting the current. If the current tends to a fall, the ballast resistance will decrease, thus permitting a larger current to flow. In order that the resistance is not affected by the speech currents, the ballast resistors are connected between each choke and the battery, and not in the lines carrying speech currents. A path must be provided for the speech currents from subscriber A to subscriber B, and this is achieved by means of the capacitors C in each line. The unbalance to earth is eliminated since *each* terminal of the battery is now isolated from the speech currents.

13.4. Sidetone

Sidetone refers to the sound a person hears in his own receiver due to his own transmission. A certain amount of sidetone is desirable, since if it is not present the speaker has the uncomfortable feeling that the telephone is not working. Too much sidetone, however, causes the speaker to lower his voice below the natural level. In the circuits so far discussed, sidetone is produced automatically, since part of the transmitter current always flows in the receiver (except in the circuit of Fig. 13.1). With modern transmitters and receivers, the amount of sidetone is usually excessive, and steps must be taken to reduce this to a more desirable level. Sidetone can be reduced by means of an auxiliary transformer, connected as shown in Fig. 13.6. This couples a

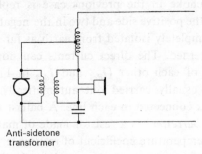

Anti-sidetone
transformer

FIG. 13.6. A method for reducing sidetone.

voltage across the receiver in such a way as to oppose the sidetone voltage. This method has been used extensively, but in more recent telephone handsets a special induction coil has been developed to reduce sidetone. This is known as the anti-sidetone induction coil (abbreviated ASTIC).

13.5. Terminating units and repeaters

Amplification of the speech signals may be necessary where the line length is in excess of a few miles. The normal two-way working of the telephone link must not be upset by the introduction of the amplifiers, and it is therefore usual to use separate amplifiers for each direction of transmission along the line. Means must be provided for separating the speech signals according to direction of transmission.

In telephone practice the complete amplifying network is termed a repeater (deriving from the fact that the output is an amplified *repeat* of the input). A repeater may therefore consist of a single valve or transistor amplifier. Where two amplifiers are combined to provide two-way amplification the combination is still termed a repeater.

Singing

Means must be provided for preventing the amplified output in one direction reaching the input of the amplifier acting in the other direction. Otherwise an oscillatory circuit may be set up, as shown in Fig. 13.7. A signal entering this circuit is amplified

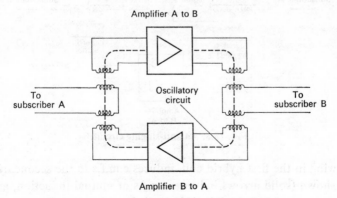

Fig. 13.7. A repeater circuit which causes singing.

continuously, and quickly builds up to a high level and may be sustained in continuous oscillation. This condition is referred to as *singing*, and can be avoided by use of a special *terminating unit* consisting basically of a *hybrid transformer* and a *balancing network* as described in the next section. Two terminating units are required at each repeater, since the repeater must behave identically in each direction.

13.6. Two- and four-wire terminations

Figure 13.8. shows one form of terminating unit, and for the purpose of description a signal is assumed to be passing from subscriber A to subscriber B. The current from subscriber A,

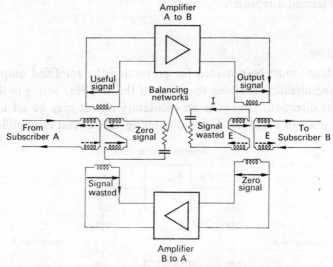

FIG. 13.8. An anti-singing circuit.

flowing in the first hybrid coil, induces e.m.f.s in the secondaries as shown (solid arrows indicate e.m.f.s of mutual-induction, and dotted arrows e.m.f.s of self-induction).

The circuit is redrawn in Fig. 13.9 where the mutually induced e.m.f.s are shown as voltage generators. It will be seen that a signal passes to the input of the A to B amplifier, and this is the useful signal. A signal is also induced across the output of the B to A amplifier, and this is wasted. In the first balancing circuit, two e.m.f.s are induced, but these are of opposing polarities and therefore cancel (assuming they are equal in magnitude).

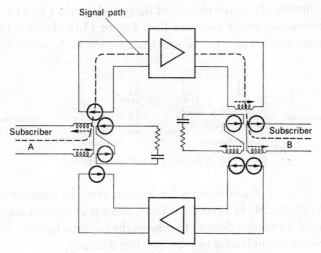

Signal path

Subscriber A

Subscriber B

FIG. 13.9. An equivalent circuit for Fig. 13.8.

Consider now the output of the A to B amplifier. A useful signal is induced in the circuit connected to subscriber B. A signal is also induced in the balancing circuit, and providing this circuit simulates exactly subscriber B's circuit, the current in the balancing network will be identical to the current in subscriber B's lines. As a result, the e.m.f.s induced in the winding connected to the input of the B to A amplifier cancel as these are arranged to be of opposite polarity. Thus a feedback circuit such as shown in Fig. 13.7 does not occur.

Since the circuits are symmetrical, a signal from B to A will be transferred in an exactly similar manner.

The transfer of signal in this way is not achieved without cost, about half the output power being dissipated in the balancing network.

Two-wire circuit

A number of repeater circuits of the type shown in Fig. 13.8 may be connected into a two-wire line. Figure 13.10 shows a block diagram for a two-wire two-repeater network. In order to be

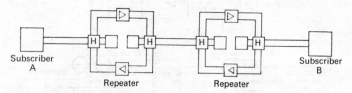

Fig. 13.10. A two-wire circuit with repeaters.

fully effective, the conditions for balance must be maintained at each hybrid coil. In practice, where a number of repeater stations are used it becomes difficult to achieve the required balance, and a four-wire circuit is used to overcome this difficulty.

Four-wire circuit

In the four-wire circuit, separate *go* and *return* paths are provided over most of the circuit. A block diagram of such a system is shown in Fig. 13.11 and it will be seen that hybrid coils are only required at the ends of the four-wire part of the circuit. Between each hybrid coil and the respective subscriber, a two-wire path is used. In this way, only two balancing networks are needed, making it easier to achieve the correct balancing conditions.

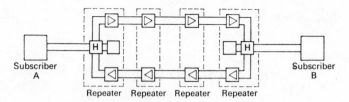

FIG. 13.11. A four-wire circuit with repeaters.

Echo

Perfect balance is rarely achieved in practice, even in the four-wire circuit shown, with the result that some signal may be fed back to a subscriber. This may not give rise to singing, as described above, but does result in the speaker receiving an *echo* of his own voice. Experience shows that if the echo is received later than about 20 msec after speaking, it causes considerable annoyance. To prevent an echo occurring, a special circuit, known as an *echo suppressor*, is required. Briefly, this is operated from the speech signals, and introduces severe attenuation in the pair of wires acting as the return path.

13.7. Exercises

1. Explain what is meant by (a) simplex operation, and (b) duplex operation, of a telephone circuit. Why are transformers used to connect the subscriber's apparatus to the lines?

2. Discuss briefly the advantages and disadvantages of (a) the local battery system, and (b) the central battery system. Which system is used in the public telephone network?

3. Explain why a transmission bridge is necessary in a modern telephone network? Describe, with the aid of a circuit diagram, the oqeration of the Stone transmission bridge.

4. By reference to a block schematic diagram, explain the equipment needed to provide a repeatered audio junction on (a) a two-wire basis, and (b) a four-wire basis. Quote typical losses for each part of the circuit. State the relative advantages of two-wire and four-wire operation. [C & G RLT A, 1962–3.]

CHAPTER 14

LINE TELEGRAPHY

14.1. Introduction

The word telegraphy is derived from two Greek words, *tele* meaning *far*, and *graphos* meaning *written*. Today, telegraphy means especially the transmission of documentary information to a distant point by electrical means. Familiar examples are telegrams, cablegrams, and picture transmission used extensively in newspaper service.

Telegraphy is the oldest form of telecommunications. As long ago as 1267, Roger Bacon, an English scientist (also accused of being a sorcerer) suggested that the magnetic properties of lodestone might be used for distant communications, and in the fifteenth and sixteenth centuries some practical telegraph systems had been made to work. In 1832 S. F. B. Morse, an American inventor, introduced his now famous dot-dash code, and in 1833 Gauss and Weber, two German mathematical physicists, invented a five-unit code upon which the codes used in present-day high-speed telegraphy are based.

The advent of telephony in 1867 replaced telegraphy for many applications. However, it was soon found that telegraphy had some distinct advantages. It can produce directly a written record of the message being transmitted and, because of its use of codes, it can utilize a very much narrower bandwidth than that required in telephony. The reduction in bandwidth is gained, however, at the expense of an increase in the time required for transmission.

As with telephony, if only a single channel is required, the lines need only be capable of handling the basic bandwidth of the signal (about 50 c/s). If a number of channels are to be provided, each signal is modulated onto a carrier assigned to it. The carrier frequencies may range from about 400 c/s to 2·5 kc/s.

14.2. Codes

A fundamental feature of all telegraph systems is the use of codes.

TABLE 14.1. THE INTERNATIONAL MORSE CODE

A · —	I · ·	R · — ·	1 · — — — —
B — · · ·	J · — — —	S · · ·	2 · · — — —
C — · — ·	K — · —	T —	3 · · · — —
D — · ·	L · — · ·	U · · —	4 · · · · —
E ·	M — —	V · · · —	5 · · · · ·
E · · — · ·	N — ·	W · — —	6 — · · · ·
F · · — ·	O — — —	X — · · —	7 — — · · ·
G — — ·	P · — — ·	Y — · — —	8 — — — · ·
H · · · ·	Q — — · —	Z — — · ·	9 — — — — ·
			0 — — — — —

Table 14.1 shows the International Morse Code, which is based on the original code invented by Morse. It will be seen that some letters require a much longer code combination than others, the letter *E* being represented by the shortest symbol, a dot. In arriving at the combinations to be used for the letters of the alphabet, Morse made a count of the frequency of letters available in a printer's office. In this way he found that letter *E* occurred more frequently than any other, and therefore allotted to *E* the shortest symbol in his code, a dot. The letter *T* he found to be the next most frequent, and therefore alloted to it the next shortest symbol, a single dash. Continuing in this way, each letter

was allotted groups of dot-dash symbols in relation to its frequency of occurrence.

It is equally important that the time interval allowed between letters, and words, and dots and dashes, be closely controlled. For example, if the interval between the dot and the dash for *A* is too long, the dot and dash may be mistaken for an *E* and *T*. The following time durations have been agreed upon internationally, the duration of one dot being taken as unit duration.

(a) One dash equal to three dots.
(b) Space between symbols forming one letter equal to one dot.
(c) Space between letters forming one word equal to three dots.
(d) Space between words equal to seven dots.

The apparatus required for sending a message in morse can be extremely simple. It is only necessary that a key be available for connecting a battery onto the transmission line for the dot-and-dash periods and which disconnects the battery for the necessary spacing periods. Some of the circuits used for morse are discussed in § 14.5. Since only two states, *on* and *off*, are required in morse, it is known as a *binary* system, the word binary signifying two. In many of the original morse systems, the *on* signal was recorded as a mark with a pen recorder, while the *off* signal was left as a space, and for this reason the two basic signalling conditions have been termed *marking* and *spacing* signals. These names are still used in modern systems where actual marks and spaces may not be recorded as such. Figure 14.1(a) shows a current–time graph for *IT IS* in morse.

The chief advantages of morse systems are:

(a) They may be operated on transmission lines having a limited bandwidth.
(b) They require manual operation which may be an advantage where urgent messages or distress signals must be sent.
(c) Morse signals can be understood in the presence of large amounts of noise.

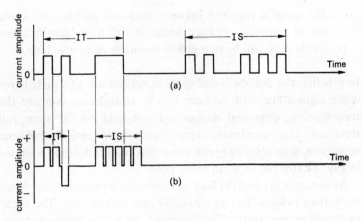

FIG. 14.1 (a) Morse code representation of *IT IS*. (b) Cable code representation of *IT IS*.

The chief disadvantage of morse is that, being manually operated, it is slow compared to machine-operated systems. Because of the uneven lengths of marks and spaces, and also because of the differing lengths of letters in the code, it is not suitable for machine telegraphy.

Cable code

This is a special form of code based on the Morse code, but instead of using a binary system, three basic signalling conditions are used. Normally these are:

(a) Negative battery to line signifies a dot.

(b) Positive battery to line signifies a dash.

(c) Earth connection to line signifies a space.

A simple method of achieving these signalling conditions is shown in Fig. 14.6.

The system therefore has the following advantages:

(a) All signalling elements can be made equal in duration.

(b) No space is required between dots and dashes since these are of opposite polarity which is sufficient identification.

(c) Cable code can be sent either manually or by machine.

In practice, the dot, dash and space durations are all equal. Three space signals are used between words. In order to improve the transmission, dots and dashes are not held on for their full duration, thus producing very short space periods between successive elements. The graph of current amplitude–time is shown in Fig. 14.1(b) for *IT IS* in cable code.

Advantages (a) and (b) lead to manually sent cable code being more than twice as fast as manually sent morse code. The speed of signalling can further be increased by using machine transmission. Cable code therefore finds extensive use, especially on submarine cables.

Cable code is essentially a d.c. system. It requires three distinct signalling conditions, and cannot be used where alternating currents, e.g. carrier waves, are involved. For radio circuits and voice-frequency telegraph circuits the cable code requires modification.

The five-unit or even-length code

A code in which each letter (or character) is represented by the same number of code elements has certain advantages, the chief one being that the design of machines for automatic sending and receiving is very much simplified. Such a code is used in the *teleprinter* (or teletypewriter) system. The teleprinter has a keyboard similar to the normal typewriter, but when the message is typed out it is automatically converted to a coded signal. At the receiving end the teleprinter converts the coded signal directly into a printed message again. Because each character is represented by the same number of code elements, the code is termed an *even-length code*. These codes also employ the *binary* system, or mark-space signals. Consider, first, a code in which each character is represented by only two signalling elements. The total number of characters possible with such a code would be four, for example:

$$A = \text{mark mark},$$
$$B = \text{space space},$$
$$C = \text{mark space},$$
$$D = \text{space mark}.$$

If each character could be represented by any combination of three signalling elements, the total number of characters possible would be eight, for example:

$$A = \text{mark mark mark},$$
$$B = \text{space space space},$$
$$C = \text{mark mark space},$$
$$D = \text{mark space space},$$
$$E = \text{space space mark},$$
$$F = \text{space mark mark},$$
$$G = \text{mark space mark},$$
$$H = \text{space mark space}.$$

In the first case, the total number of characters is given by 2^2. In the second case by 2^3.

In general, for a binary, or two-state code, which uses n elements for each character, the total number of characters possible is

$$2^n. \qquad (14.1)$$

In order to cover the requirements of the English alphabet, each character must be represented by at least five elements. This gives a total of

$$2^5 = 32 \text{ characters}, \qquad (14.2)$$

which is more than sufficient for the 26 letters of the alphabet. However, this number is not sufficient to cover numerals as well as letters. The difficulty is overcome by using two of the 32 combinations as *shift signals*. One is a *letter-shift* signal, which when transmitted sets the receiving mechanism so that all following signals are printed as letters (with the exception of the second shift signal). The second shift signal is known as a *figure-shift* signal, and when this is transmitted it sets the receiving mechanism to print figures for succeeding groups of signals (except, of course, for the letter-shift signal). In this way a total of 60 characters is available, which covers the alphabet, numerals and provides for commas, full stops, etc.

As with the morse code, international codes have been agreed upon for five-unit systems. Two codes are employed: (i) the International Telegraph Alphabet No. 1, which is used in systems where the operator converts the message to code using a keyboard having five keys, for example the Baudot Multiplex System; (ii) the International Telegraph Alphabet No. 2, which is used

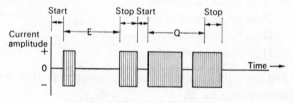

FIG. 14.2. The letters *E* and *Q* in the teleprinter start–stop code.

for teleprinter operation. In this code, each group of five elements must be preceded by a start element, which is a space, and followed by a stop element, which is a mark, but which may be equal in duration to one and a half units. Thus although referred to as a five-unit code, each character requires from 7 to $7\frac{1}{2}$ units of time, depending on the length of the stop element. Figure 14.2 shows two letters in the start–stop code, and the corresponding current waveform, using a carrier wave.

14.3. Telegraph speed

The speed at which messages can be transmitted is obviously an important consideration in any telegraph system. As a measure of speed, words per minute (w.p.m.) forms a useful guide, but it is not exact enough from an engineering viewpoint. Telegraph speed is defined in terms of the shortest unit used in the code, and is simply the number of shortest units which may be transmitted in one second. The unit of speed is termed the *Baud*, and is so named after E. Baudot, a French telegraph engineer, who contributed much to telegraphy.

As an example, in the teleprinter code, marks and spaces are equal in duration, and either forms a basic unit, or element, in the code. In some teleprinter machines the duration of a mark or a space is 20 msec, and therefore the telegraph speed is

$$\frac{1}{0 \cdot 02} = 50 \text{ Bauds.}$$

In such a machine the speed is constant at this value, and is independent of the number of words per minute transmitted. The speed in Bauds enables the *maximum* speed in words per minute to be estimated, but assumptions have to be made regarding the number of letters to a word and the spacing allowed between words. Assuming that an average English word has five letters, and that a space equal in duration to one letter is allowed between words, then each word requires an average of six characters. In the teleprinter code, each character requires 5 units plus a start unit, plus a stop equal to one and a half units, i.e. a total of $7\frac{1}{2}$ units. Therefore the average word requires

$$7\frac{1}{2} \times 6 \text{ units}$$
$$= 45 \text{ units.}$$

Therefore the maximum speed in w.p.m. at a machine speed of

50 Bauds is

$$\frac{50 \times 60}{45}$$

$$= 66\frac{2}{3} \text{ w.p.m.}$$

The actual speed in w.p.m. may be less than this, of course, depending on the actual time allowed between words, etc.

As another example, the shortest unit in Morse is the dot. As seen previously, the characters in Morse have unequal numbers of dots and dashes, therefore a further assumption must be made regarding the number of shortest units per character. This is usually taken as being equal to 9 dots. Therefore the number of dots required for a typical word is $(5 \times 9) + 7 = 52$, the 7 dots being the agreed spacing between words in Morse. If the signal is being sent at n w.p.m., the number of shortest elements per second, which is also the speed in Bauds, is

$$\frac{n \times 52}{60}$$

$$= n \times 0.866 \text{ Bauds.}$$

Word speeds of up to 30 w.p.m. can be achieved in practice, and assuming 30 w.p.m. to be the upper limit, the speed in Bauds for morse is 26 Bauds. Unlike machine telegraphy, this value is not fixed, but relies on the w.p.m. speed. At a word speed of 15 w.p.m., the telegraph speed is 13 Bauds.

14.4. Relationship between telegraph speed and bandwidth

There is a fundamental law which states that the frequency bandwidth required for the transmission of any signal is proportional to the speed at which it is transmitted. As an example consider a gramophone record being played at its normal speed. If the highest frequency in the recording is 10,000 c/s, the record player must be capable of passing this frequency. If the speed is doubled, the highest frequency will also be doubled, and the record player must pass frequencies up to 20,000 c/s, i.e. the bandwidth is doubled. Looked at in another way, it can be seen that if the bandwidth is doubled, the time required for transmission is halved, since in the example quoted the record would only run for half its normal running time.

An exchange of time and bandwidth is a disadvantage where it affects the message, as in the example given. But in the transmission medium where the message is in the form of an electrical signal, such an exchange may be used to advantage. This is especially true of telegraphy.

An estimate of the bandwidth required for a signal of given telegraph speed can be obtained in the following simplified manner. Figure 14.3 shows a telegraph signal which consists of a succession of alternate marks and spaces. Each mark and succeeding space is approximately equal to one cycle of the sinusoidal variation, shown dashed in Fig. 14.3. Let the telegraph speed

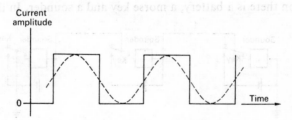

FIG. 14.3. Used to estimate bandwidth.

be n Bauds, then there will be a total of n marks and spaces transmitted per second, since each mark or space corresponds to a basic unit. There will be $\frac{1}{2}n$ *pairs* of marks and spaces per second, or $\frac{1}{2}n$ c/s of the sinusoidal variation. It is important to note that this is for d.c. telegraphy, i.e. where a mark signal is represented by direct current "on" the line and a space signal by an "off" period of equal duration. Assuming that the lowest frequency is zero corresponding to zero speed, the bandwidth required for d.c. telegraphy is given by

$$B = \tfrac{1}{2}n \text{ c/s, where } n \text{ is speed in Bauds.} \qquad (14.3)$$

In Chapter 4 it was shown that where modulation is used, sidebands each equal in width to the basic bandwidth, are produced on both sides of the carrier. Therefore the total bandwidth required when the basic signal is used to modulate a carrier wave is

$$B = 2 \times \tfrac{1}{2}n$$
$$= n \text{ c/s} \qquad (14.4)$$

14.5. Basic telegraph circuits

Single current simplex

The simplest Morse telegraph systems are shown in Figs. 14.4 and 14.5. Figure 14.4 is known as an *open-circuit system*. At each station there is a battery, a morse key and a sounder. In the early

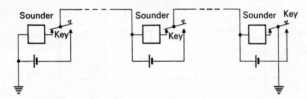

FIG. 14.4. Simplex Morse circuit — open circuit.

Morse systems, the sounder was a device in which a hammer was caused to strike a bell when a dot was received and to strike a metal plate when a dash was received. Thus the code element was recognized by a distinctive sound.

It was soon discovered, however, that operators could recognize dots and dashes merely by means of the time interval between the sounds, so that two distinctive sounds were unnecessary. Thus was developed the Morse sounder which was used for many years on all main telegraph routes.

In the open-circuit system of Fig. 14.4 the morse key acts as a two-way switch which, in the inoperative position, connects the station sounder to the line. When it is desired to transmit, the key is depressed, which disconnects the sounder at the transmitting station, and at the same time connects the battery to the line. The key is held down for a period corresponding to a dot or dash and is released for the corresponding character space or word space, before it is depressed again. In this system (used mainly in Europe), a battery is required at each station, but the line only carries current when a transmission takes place.

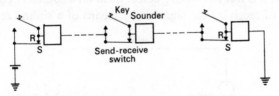

FIG. 14.5. Simplex Morse circuit – closed circuit.

The closed circuit system of Fig. 14.5 is used mostly in the U.S.A. It will be seen that only one battery is required, and thus battery maintenance costs are considerably reduced. This saving is partly offset, however, by the fact that the current flows in the line, except when interrupted for transmission and thus power consumption is increased. On long lines, additional batteries will also be required. In this system, the morse key acts as a simple on–off switch, but in addition to a key, each station requires a send–receive switch. When a station is not sending, this switch must be left in the receive position, otherwise the telegraph link is open-circuited. When it is desired to transmit from a station, the operator opens the send–receive switch. On depressing the key for dots and dashes, current flows, which in turn operates the sounders at the other stations. The key is left up, or open, for the correct spacing intervals between dots and dashes, and thus no current flows during the spacing periods. Both of the systems described are known generally as *single current simplex* systems. Single current denotes that current only flows one way along the line, from a given sender, and simplex denotes that only one message can be sent at a time.

Cable code simplex

In cable code, dots and dashes are distinguished by different polarities of current, i.e. current flowing one way signifies a dot and flowing the other way signifies a dash. Since they are of equal duration, it is not possible to detect them on a sounder. The usual method of receiving the signal is by means of a siphon recorder.

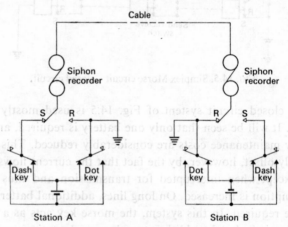

FIG. 14.6. Cable code simplex circuit.

Figure 14.6 shows a simplified circuit for cable code simplex operation. Each station requires two keys—one for dots and one for dashes. A send–receive switch and a battery are also required at each station. When neither station is sending, the send–receive switch must be left in the receive position, which connects an earth to the cable at both ends. Consider now station A transmitting. The send–receive switch is first moved to the send position, but the earth connection to the cable at A is maintained through the dot and dash keys. When the dash key is depressed the earth circuit to the cable is broken, and the negative of the battery is connected instead. Current flows from the battery at A through the dot key to earth, and hence through the earth circuit to station B; from station B through the siphon recorder, and the cable, to the siphon recorder at A, and back to the battery at A through the dash key. When the dot key is depressed, the negative of the battery at A is connected to earth. Current flows out of the battery through the dash key at A, around the same circuit, and back to the battery through earth. It will be seen that at station B the battery connections are reversed. This ensures that the direction of line current is the same for code elements of the same kind, irrespective of which station is transmitting.

Phantom circuit

This method of connection enables a telegraph circuit to use existing telephone lines without there being any mutual interference between telephone and telegraph signals.

In the phantom circuit of Fig. 14.7, earth forms one connection for the telegraph circuit, the other connection being made through

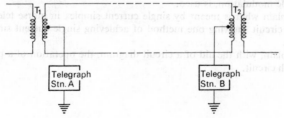

FIG. 14.7. A phantom telegraph circuit.

the centre taps on the telephone transformers. Consider telegraph station A transmitting. The telegraph current divides in opposite directions through the secondary of telephone transformer T_1, therefore the induced e.m.f.s in the primary due to the telegraph signal cancel. The telegraph signal current flows out along both telephone wires, and merges again at the secondary of the telephone transformer T_2. Again, because the currents in the secondary are in opposite directions, the e.m.f.s induced in the primary due to the telegraph signal cancel.

The speech signal is carried over the wires in the normal manner, as described in § 13.2. No speech currents will flow through the telegraph circuit provided the telephone lines and the centre taps are balanced, since there will then be no potential difference at speech frequencies between the centre taps.

14.6. Exercises

1. Explain briefly why codes are essential in all telegraph systems. List the relative advantages and disadvantages of Morse code, cable code, and the five-unit even-length code.

2. Explain what is meant by a binary code. What is the minimum number of elements that must be used in an even-length binary code, to represent one character for a message in English?

3. Define what is meant by telegraph speed in Bauds. A teleprinter transmits at a rate of 400 characters per minute. If each character requires $7\frac{1}{2}$ units in the code, calculate the telegraph speed in Bauds.

4. State the fundamental law relating telegraph speed and bandwidth. Determine, for the teleprinter transmission in Ex. 3, the theoretical bandwidth required when (a) d.c. telegraphy is used and (b) carrier telegraphy, employing amplitude modulation, is used.

5. Explain what is meant by single current simplex in morse telegraphy. Draw a circuit showing one method of achieving single current simplex in practice.

6. Explain, with the aid of a circuit diagram, the operation of a phantom telegraph circuit.

ANSWERS TO EXERCISES

§ 1.10

1. (a) 3·32 m; (b) 1·11 m; (c) 3·32 cm.   **2.** 15 m; 5 m; 1·5 m; 90 m.   **4.** 5000 Mc/s.   **7.** 24 min.

§ 2.9

1. (a) 20 dB; 48 dB; −46 dB; (b) 6 dB; 8·68 dB; −40 dB; (c) 20 dB; 48dB; −46 dB;   **2.** 27 dB.   **3.** (a) 7 dBm; (b) 5 mW; (c) 20 mW.   **4.** 3 dB.
5. (a) 21 dB; (b) 21 dB.

§ 3.5

1. 250 c/s; 750 c/s; 1250 c/s.   **2.** 5th to 16th inclusive.   **3.** 200 c/s; 400 c/s; 600 c/s.

§ 4.7

1. 9 kc/s; 501·5–505·95 kc/s, and 506 kc/s, and 506·5–510·5 kc/s.   **2.** (a) 30%; (b) 0·15 V.   **3.** (a) 100 kc/s; (b) 10 kc/s; (c) 50%.   **4.** 10 V at 50 kc/s; 0·5 V at 51 kc/s and 49 kc/s; 0·05 V at 52 kc/s and 48 kc/s.

§ 6.6

1. 318 kc/s.   **2.** (a) 504 kc/s; (b) 1·0 Ω.   **3.** (a) 10 kc/s; (b) 1·77 mA.

§ 7.9

4. 120 mA; 13 mA; −11 mA.   **5.** 8·9 mV.

§ 8.21

11. 25; 5·0 mA/V; 5·0 kΩ.

§ 10.13

2. $I_a = 11\cdot4$ mA; $V_a = 185$ V; (a) ±4 mA; (b) 35.   **3.** $I_e = 1\cdot72$ mA; $V_{ce} = 6\cdot25$ V; ±0·8 mA; ±2·25 V.

§ 11.9

1. 105–421 pF.

§ 14.6

3 50 Bauds.   **4.** 25 c/s; 50 c/s.

INDEX

PRINTED IN HUNGARY